Reckoning 6

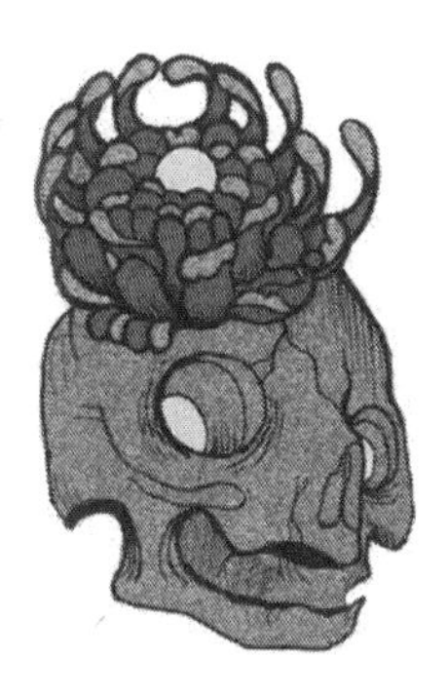

Reckoning 6
Electronic Edition: Winter 2022
Poetry Editor: Aïcha Martine Thiam
Prose Editor: Gabriela Santiago

Reckoning *is a communal effort.*
Editorial staff, in alphabetical order:

Noa Covo
Priya Chand
Michael J. DeLuca
Joseph Hope
Justin Howe
Andrew Kozma
Giselle K. Leeb
Johannes Punkt
Catherine Rockwood

Cover and interior ornament by Zuzanna Kwiecien

Reckoning Press
206 East Flint Street
Lake Orion, MI 48362
www.reckoning.press
distributed by IngramSpark
printed by Book Mobile
on 100% post-consumer recyled paper.

 ISSN 2474-7327
e-ISBN 978-1-955360-03-6
ISBN 978-1-955360-04-3

Contents

Cover:
A Dream I Have

Zuzanna Kwiecien

Zuzanna is an illustrator and designer. She aims to capture the visual narrative of the subject and combine it with a distinct atmosphere. As an artist, she val□es time and effort p□t into the constr□ction of a high-quality work of art.

From the Editors: **On Making Peace With Time When Time Has Lost All Meaning**

Aïcha Martine Thiam

I have resisted writing a Pandemic [insert "poem/story/essay/play/song"] just as I have resisted writing a BLM [____], or a #MeToo [____]. Those borders, those things that can be designated and specificated have given me pa□se as far as I can remember.

In part it comes from perpetual rage: I want to write about all the worldwide historical injustices faced by Black women, about all the times powerful structures have failed marginalized people during globalized socioeconomic collapses. I want to write about all the moments when being alive on this planet felt like boarding an unsound ship.

When one lives in a tottering world, within a body and an identity frequently threatened, between multiple cultures that blurry the notion of belonging, and in an age that often disappoints in mundane, comical ways, the refusal to moor oneself to a place, any place, can be (ironically) grounding. Liberating, at the very least; because when everything feels terrible, as it too frequently does, it comes heavy. Immobilizing.

I have resisted, because surely, I tell myself, we are more than the random era into which we have been tossed together. The stories we tell are universal (the cyclical nature of History being some proof of this), similar accounts and heartaches reverberating simultaneously in every curious pocket of the world. How else to explain how the same folktale can pop up across unrelated cultures? How a same chord progression can transcend cent□ries and completely different instruments?

I imagine there's vanity in there too: if I don't point out when this particular story emerged in me, then perhaps in a thousand years, someone can consider it as a free and formless thing. Perhaps this story can live forever.

When pondering the Poetry and Nonfiction call for submissions for Reckoning 6, then, I deferred to that old determination: *do* not *say pandemic-inspired, do* not *say 2020 racial injustice protests, or climate change school strike.* Nothing, in short, that would contract the scope to this here Moment. If we received those pieces, all the better, because of course I wanted them: but mostly, I hoped for those everyday experiences that transcended the greedy enclosures of Time. The seething meditations, the exhaustion exhalations, those rooted anguishes that come barreling down each person's generational road.

These Major Historical Events: they seemingly confine suffering + its company (faith, grief, clarity, disillusionment) to the dates that anchor them, as if that is where they *generally* start. Reflexively, the eye starts to look forward, for that other part, the end date, that indicates where it *generally* tapers off. It becomes a shorthand. There is an immediate accounting neither for those subtleties, nor for the enormity of every moment when something similarly calamitous—albeit quieter—has occurred.

These Major Historical Events: too often seen as catalysts, relegated to cause and effect, too *seldom* seen as uncoverers of what has always been there. We talk of colonization and the Civil Rights Movement and environmental racism as if the date of their coining effectively gave them more concrete life; as if everything that came before, the collection of separate events creating the momentum, were only leading up to that eruptive movement. As if everything after were merely the comedown from that Really Big Thing. If anything, it is convenient for those who are unwilling to recognize the constancy of injustice.

Even as a child, ever the cynic, I side-eyed the promises from the powers that be, instigated by the summit or protest of the day, knowing that even without them, the unglamorous and steady fight would go on. Knowing that when the moment passed, so too would the cacophonous and shallow empathy.

Maybe unfair, but I said I was a cynic.

It's why I've done away with tangible places and dates in my stories, chasing instead the tantalizing flavors of uchronias, analogies, multiverses.

It's why I've given in to the jolt of recognition when yet another person in the last two years declared "time has lost all meaning!"—*my people! join the club!*

It's why I have worshipped any device that thumbed its nose at temporality, be it ghost stories and reincarnation and fortune telling, or a certain wibbly-wobbly, timey-wimey flying police box.

But as most childhood cynicism goes, surprise, surprise: it buckles at first encounter with something so utterly unlike itself. My, how the poems and essays in this issue have proven me wrong. They are blazingly loud and searingly quiet and yes, funny, even. They are a sight to behold.

In a way, this call for submissions did more than I could have hoped for: namely it gave us devastating works of art that, borderless, might as well be speaking to a broad, almost abstract humanity.

But, it was also profoundly, unexpectedly humbling to challenge the notion that freezing a moment might reduce the scope of its significance: I sometimes forget how much it can intensify and honor it. We asked for environmental justice at the intersection of social justice—and indeed, every historical event existing under that umbrella is established, constant, neverending.

And yet, each poem, each essay, each story we got tells of what it meant, at *that* time, to *that* specific author. Every word, every line entrenched in the minutes, months, and eons that marked those who wrote them; in the specificity of a prancing second, in the gaping parentheses of a noteworthy couple of years. They make profound etches on the authors' respective soft surfaces: I was There and Then. Whether about fleeting long-ago liminalities, emotions pinioned by constant rumination, or yes, even pandemic-inspired thoughts, they radiate Time.

Profoundly, unexpectedly humbling: to be reminded that it is not only futile, but also inadvisable to the integrity of a story, to try to disregard the weight of the moment that made it.

Just as too many people I love remember every setback—financial, emotional, personal—felt in the last co□ple of years; j□st as I remember every instance when my mother was told to go back to her country; just as the Lac Rose in Dakar remembers every foot that tickled its shores; so does this planet we're on, surely, remember every time it was sorely wounded.

Cruel Time. Strange Time. Funny Time.

To any and all who need an overdue reconciliation with this baffling notion, I hope that this bea□tif□l collection gives yo□ a helping hand.

I still eye Time with suspicion, still dodge specifying questions; but making peace with it doesn't seem so uncanny lately.

I imagine it's like a brief closing of the hand around something small and floating, framing it j□st long eno□gh that we are able to look, really look at it. And then, if we can, we let it go.

Aïcha Martine is a trilingual/multicultural writer, musician and artist, and might have been a kraken in a past life. She's an editor at *Reckoning*, co-EIC/Producer/Creative Director of *The Nasiona*, and has been nominated for Best of the Net, The Best Small Fictions and The Pushcart Prize. She is the author of *At Sea* (*CLASH BOOKS*), which was shortlisted for the 2019 *Kingdoms in the Wild* Poetry Prize, and her second collection, *BURN THE WITCH*, is forthcoming with *Finishing Line Press*. Some words fo□nd in: *Déraciné, The Rumpus, Moonchild Magazine, Marías at Sampaguitas, Luna Luna, Bright Wall/Dark Room, Pussy Magic, South Broadway Ghost Society, Gone Lawn, Boston Accent Lit, Anti-Heroin Chic, Cosmonauts Avenue, Tenderness Lit.* @Maelllstrom/ www.amartine.com.

From the Editors

What We Have At the End of the World

Gabriela Santiago

In a way, hope is a failure of imagination. In a way, it is a flo□rishing.

It is a failure because I cannot imagine the end. The world goes on, and on and on, even when we wish it would stop.

I know how bad it is. The emission levels, the microplastics, the pipelines, the species gone, the rogue genes introduced, the coral dying, the water rising. The infrastructure still damaged in Puerto Rico when I visit my great-□ncle, the dro□ghts and floods within the same week that destroy the soil of my mother's farm in Illinois, a tornado in a Minnesotan December as I leave another message on my senator's voicemail. I know.

But the end? That I cannot comprehend. There is a well of despair so deep I could fall forever, there is a grief so all-consuming it warps the edges of dimensions, melts reality like plastic trash on a campfire. Who co□ld wrap their mind aro□nd that loss?

I am only human. I can only hold one emotion for so long.

In a way, hope is a flo□rishing of imagination. Beca□se when we reject the surrender of the end, we must imagine going on in new ways. And there is no limit to the paths the authors have chosen in answering this submission call for complexity, complicity, and hope.

Always hope.

We become trees, exhaling oxygen and digging our roots into eroding shores; we become islands, and rise up. We endow the soil itself with artificial intelligence and willingly place o□r fate in its hands. We speak with fungi, and we speak with our family, and all of the conversations are hard and necessary. We grapple with a monstrous, enduring capitalism, and reach out for each other as it tries to trap us within ourselves. Even when we are no longer on the planet, there are echoes of us and our actions in the relationships of the lives, natural and mechanical, we leave behind. We become ghosts but it never stops mattering that we were here, that we did what we could.

We go on and on and on. Together.

It is not utopia. But it is what we can have, these careful negotiations, communications, challenges, and sharing. We have relationships. New, complicated, frustrating, rewarding. Alive.

Relationships are what we have at the end of the world. The world is ending right now.

Hello. Nice to meet you. Please sit down. Are you warm? I have made my mother's herbal tea. I have made soup from a local butcher and a CSA. I have made cookies from lard and wheat flo□r and s□gar whose history is drenched in blood; they sparkle in the light. Please eat. It's cold outside, for now. Tell me what you imagine.

The world is also beginning.

Gabriela Santiago is a writer and performer based in St. Paul, Minnesota. A graduate of the Clarion writing workshop and a proud member of Team Tiny Bonesaw, she has been published in *Clarkesworld, Strange Horizons, The Dark, Lightspeed, Nightmare,* and *Lady Churchill's Rosebud Wristlet*, among others. She is the founder and curator of Revolutionary Jetpacks, a science fiction cabaret centering visions of the f□t□re by BIPOC, queer and trans, and disabled artists. You can follow her @LifeOnEarth89 or writing-relatedactivities.tumblr.com.

Resilience

Francesca Gabrielle Hurtado

They called us resilient.

They think it only means *strong*.
They say the Filipino Spirit is all positivity,
is smiling when the storm hits,
is finding the light in the darkness,
no matter what.
They don't know that daybreak finds us
shadowed and shaking,
breaking and almost broken,
caked in dirt and the debris of someone else's
irresponsibility.
Because when the storm hits,
it brings us to our knees.
Witness, then,
the concavity of a body,
wide open and aching,
gasping in the sunlight,
spilt on the earth.

We are god's poison-tasters,
bitten off by the teeth,
bitten off at the skin.
Purpled by the dawn, we are
shivering for want and waiting
for something that feels like justice.
We take refuge in the rock piles,
drunk on earthquakes and
fermented in cheap grace,
tooth by tooth,
flesh by pound of tender flesh;
we would give anything
not to disassemble in the echo
of a careless politician's footsteps.

Find us howling
where mangrove meets with salted water,
nursing from the sea,
hands clasped in prayer,
throat aching for prayer to be enough,
eyes anguished with supplication.
We are human splinters,
scattered by the flood,
by the fire,
by the shaking of the earth,
by the blood on the pavement,
in the cracks of the land,
on the stones of the mountain,
caked underneath the fingernails
of all the strongmen who so desperately want
to be strong men.
They know *nothing* of the Filipino Spirit.
They only know what their greed whispers to their dirty hearts.
They cannot see us coming undone.
They choose not to see us coming undone.

And yet here we are,
eroded with every new tempest,
bleeding our runoff into an ocean of time,
knuckles splitting on the door of
an indifferent god,
our mezzanines shattered,
our columns felled,
our temples all defeated.
We are children to this anger,
this hateful neglect of a people,
this ageless war for the soul of a nation
that has not learned yet how to love itself
without devouring its own.

And so here we are,
leveled in the beat of the earth,
still holding on to everything,

still trying to call this ragged country home.
In this flowerfield of wreckage,
find ⊡s crying into empty c⊡ps,
mouths waiting
for a hot meal,
for a garden song,
for a kind word to say about the state of our nation,
or else for a war cry.
For a call to arms.
The Filipino Spirit demands
that we be strong,
not only in defeat or in darkness,
but in the disobedient thundering of our hearts
in a clamor for our due.

Remember this:
we grew from seeds.
We hid in the cracks of the land and
let the storms make us brave, not broken.
We let the lightning carve our grief into good intentions
and we refused to call them scars.
We are the better tomorrow,
the lesson learned,
we are the light in the darkness,
the way home, resplendent
even in our disrepair.

This is us. This is resilience.
This is the Filipino Spirit,
unyielding and unbroken.

Francesca is a queer Filipino writer who has a degree in Architecture, with a specialty in Tropical Architecture. Her writing background leans towards poetry and essay-writing, but lately she's been working on writing her own epic fantasy novel. Her work aims to highlight issues of justice, in the way people interact with each other and with the world around them. She also paints watercolours and does calligraphy. P.S. She loves dragons.

Move, Mountain, Move

Russell Nichols

To those who can't stand
the rain:

let it flow
and move mountains.

cry me a spout
for watered mustard seeds
to sprout from well-tended
gardens of grief,
eroding rocks, making hard
places bend to the will
of irrigated tear ducts.

cry me a mountain range
so i can measure variations
in river steepness and rainfall
and calculate the pain
carved in your rugged terrain.

do not blame yourself.
fault the tectonics that try
to shame your way of weathering
and take credit for relief.

there is no relief without release,
says science.

so cry me a new topography
with contours that naturally defy
convention and gravity in the same weep.

let it flow
let it flow
let it flow

from mountains high to valleys low
let us make a new earth.

oh to be

Russell Nichols

oh to be breathing
in a strange
land of strangulation
shown from different
angles where extreme degrees
of difficulty make it harder
to draw anything other
than a gun

oh to be one
with the lung of the universe
expanding... inhaling the charred
steak of dead stars, kicking up red
dust on Mars in the pale faces
of fear and dread

oh to be an engineer
that makes diagrams of diaphragms
to invent new ventilators
for post-reconstruction purposes
available for delivery
at premature
funeral services

oh to be mother
nature's summer lover so every
time she takes my breath away,
i know it won't
be forever

oh to be like the trees
that synthesize the light of day
leaving without leaving

oh to be

oh to be alive
again

oh
to
be

oh to
oh to
oh to
oh to
oh to
oh to
oh to
oh to

R□ssell Nichols is a spec□lative fiction writer and endangered jo□rnalist. Raised in Richmond, California, he got rid of all his st□ff in 2011 to live out of a backpack with his wife, vagabonding around the world ever since. Look for him at russellnichols.com.

Surprise

Tom Barlow

My hometown was already a wreck by the
time I arrived. Nimishillen Creek ran

motor oil and sewer slops behind the
high school, and downtown disappeared in

smoke the day fathers lit their coal furnaces.
Deer and bluebirds were as rare as the

people who worried about the deer and
the bluebirds, and we hurled beer cans

onto the roadside like our heroes threw
hand grenades. We rode our motorbikes

up and down the slag heaps left us by
the strip miners who took their money

and moved as far away as they could afford
from the ruin that funded their move, and

there was joy everywhere in the conviction
that America went on forever and nothing

we could do would ever fill it up.

Surprise.

Tom Barlow is an Ohio author of poetry, short stories and novels. His work has appeared in journals and anthologies including *PlainSongs, Ekphrastic Review, Voicemail Poetry, Hobart, Tenemos, Redivider, Aji The New York Quarterly, The Modern Poetry Quarterly,* and many more. See more at tombarlowauthor.com.

Babang Luksa

Nicasio Andres Reed

Salt had crept in while he was away, and now the freshwater wetlands of Gino's childhood are a marsh, brackish and fickle. There is the soccer field where he'd stained his knees; it had been a low, dry rise of earth bracketed by mud and cordgrass, and today is impassable, a thicket of cattails in algae-skinned water, a humming choir of insects. And here the Jiffy Lube where Gino got his first job, and the stand of trees outside it where Gino smoked his first cigarettes. A line of fat, old maples that in the summer had dropped their seeds in spinning helicopter wings by the whirling hundreds, and in the autumn had lit up like matchheads, screaming into the sky. First week of June now, and they're not doing much of anything, their branches almost bare, bark corpse-grey from drinking saltwater. Around the corner to Mifflin St, past the stripped bones of the gas station, up two blocks to the high tide line at the sandbagged steps of the Shop & Go, the empty lot opposite repurposed into a dock for the neighborhood fleet: half a dozen rowboats with their oars padlocked athwart, one eight-seater bowrider with yellowing upholstery, one jet ski, and, as they come into dock, the roofed pontoon that Gino caught a ride on, a Habitat for Humanity donation.

"Forty." Benji, the helmsman.

"Get outta here." Gino, sucking his teeth.

"We got a problem?"

"Nah, man. Nah." Gino digs out his wallet.

"Cash."

"Yeah, I figured. Y'all getting a lotta outages?"

Benji counts through the ones and fives. "More power outages than power. We on generators, if we on."

"Shit."

Benji shakes his head. "Is what it is. You need directions?"

"I'm good, thanks. I grew up around here."

The boardwalk from the boats to dry asphalt is made of wooden shipping pallets, new ones stacked on top of old when they've started to molder as the mud takes them. Gino slings his bag over his shoulder and walks across with his eyes on his feet, distrustful of the dark patches where it looks rotted through. The street is a relief, even with sedge and woolgrass cutting up through cracks in the pavement for the first few yards past the waterline.

The distance from the Stop & Go to his childhood home is the length of time it took to eat a bag of spicy pork skins and throw the evidence in a neighbor's garbage can so his mom wouldn't know he'd been ruining his dinner. But he'd measured it in a teenage boy's appetite, and the walk seems quicker now. The streets narrower, the telephone poles shorter, the sky closer, everything more squat, and the gritty smell of the marsh clinging on even two blocks up the street. Still, it's late in the afternoon and the sun on the clouds is starting to blush, so folks are setting themselves up on front stoops in threes and sixes with cigarettes and beer bottles and babies on bouncing knees, their friendly racket sounding to Gino something like a first language, so familiar, unheard for years. He gets a couple nods and throws them back, but nobody knows him on sight.

He turns the corner onto S Bonsall St. The sidewalk is broken in all the same spots he didn't know he knew until he sees them again, and then he knows every fissure and crack, every dog paw immortalized in wet cement. No parked cars. A lot more boarded-up doors and windows than there used to be, although there'd always been some. There were never any front yards in the neighborhood, all the basement windows looking directly out onto the sidewalk. Now every house on the row that still looks occupied has a rain barrel out front, and a couple have one of those larger, galvanized metal cisterns that look like fat little grain silos. There's a line of grass growing right down the middle of the street. Sedge, probably—a bad sign on what used to be high ground.

And then, inevitably, there's #2017. He's been gone almost twenty years and it looks... not the same, but like a faded photograph of itself. Gino doesn't know if it's looked like that for a while, or if it happened all at once. If a year ago, when his father died, the color drained from the house's façade. He could still turn around.

It's not that he hasn't thought about his father's death, or how it would be to come home and see the place without him. But he's been able to think about it from a distance, know it without seeing it. And that's worked out for him, overall. But from the bottom of the steps and through the screen door, there's his mother's voice telling someone to bring out the good plates, the ones for company. So much clearer than her voice over the phone, telling him she'd understand if he couldn't make the trip, like she was forgiving him for disappointing her even before he did it.

Gino wants very much to be someone who doesn't need to be forgiven. So, up the stairs he goes.

Gino was five years old when the bulge of the Schuylkill River met the fattened trickle of Cobb's Creek to the east, and together they fingered their way west through parkways and backyards to touch the glutted Delaware. It was then declared that everything south of the Roosevelt Expressway was officially part of the greater Chesapeake floodplain. The majority of Philadelphia was under at least six inches of water, so the entirety of it was legally classified as inundated. The news, his folks, everyone adult he knew, kept track of the losses. The city took bids on where to relocate the Liberty Bell, and crowdfunded the removal and transport of the arch at the foot of Chinatown. The neighborhood threw up barriers around the Pentecostal church on Snyder Ave, and bought up and replanted mangroves from nurseries on the Jersey shore. They were losing more ground than they saved, though, for as long as he could remember.

When he was eight, the block half a mile away where his mom grew up was evacuated, and his grandpop moved in with them, slept on the couch. His sharp-pressed slacks and red-striped shirts displaced Gino's clothes in the closet. His basketball games and bocce club pushed Gino out of the afternoons he'd spent with his dad. And his voice, old Philly, short vowels running up into each other, filtered into every room and out the front door onto the stoop, every day adding to his eulogy for the city. Grief was the background static of Gino's childhood—everyone else's grief for a place he'd never been.

Gino's family's place was in West Passyunk, a little too distant from the heart of old Italian Philadelphia to benefit from touristy nostalgia, and too Black and brown for their one sob story among many to generate charitable donations. Like for the Black folks down in Kingsessing, up in Kensington, the official plan was to leave it to rot in the water. But the less-than-a-mile-square from 20th St to 26th sat on a rise known only to kids who'd biked it, pushing and sweating up one way and gliding, legs storked out, down the other. While the rest of the neighborhood went to algae and rot, Gino's old block and the couple dozen around it became an island in the marsh.

It was almost lucky. A mile in any direction, the government offered to buy homeowners out of their property for less than a quarter of how much it would cost them to start over somewhere further inland. Most people took it because, in the choice between an insultingly low offer and nothing at all, they figured it was better not to wait around for the insulting offer to expire. Up in the neighborhood, basements flooded, tap water went funny, electricity flickered and failed, but no buy-out offers came. And even as everything else changed, the old rule held true: if you didn't get out of the neighborhood by the time you were eighteen, then chances were you were never getting out.

Gino left when he was eighteen. Gino's older brother Stevie got married at eighteen. Stevie's in his forties now, and on the couch this morning, his knees as high as his chest because his spot in the far corner has sagged under the years he's spent there. There's a stack of dishes and cutlery on the coffee table in front of him. He's the ghost of their dad: heavy brows, a twice-broken nose, an ancient, thick sweater despite the heat, and a smile that'll never let you in on the joke. More him than their mom, so more Filipino than Italian, and Gino, never pegged as either, remembers again to resent him for it.

"Jesus, you actually showed," Stevie says to him. There's a pause where Gino's supposed to say something biting, but he doesn't rise to it. Stevie shrugs. "You got about a minute to turn around and leave before the rest notice you're here."

"Eugenio." Stevie's husband, frozen halfway down the stairs. "Got some fuckin nerve showing up here."

"Kevin," Gino says. He hasn't set his bag down yet. "You look good. Change your hair?"

"Don't tell me how I fuckin look you—"

"Gino!" His name ricochets down the hall and around the kitchen, then back out into the living room, carried on the high voices of his nieces who make him hug them. One of them takes his bag upstairs, whispering something strident to her dad on the way. Jasmine, Gino thinks. The one with the freckles is Jasmine, and the other one is Roxie, who's telling him about what they're making in the kitchen, what they had to substitute in the pancit, and what they grew in the community garden. Cousins, assorted children, and neighborhood aunties and their husbands cycle into the room with dry kisses and slaps on the shoulder, telling him he hasn't changed at all, telling him he's gained weight. Kevin slips behind them all and into the kitchen, and Gino tells everyone that he needs to go volunteer to help out his mom before word spreads that he rolled up to her house expecting to stand around being waited on.

He steps heavy down the short hall back to the kitchen, less to give Kevin and his mom warning he's coming, and more to spare himself whatever they were saying about him. Which might have been a sound strategy, in another family.

"Don't know why he bothered," Kevin is saying. From less of a distance now, Gino can see the white in his hair, and that the pinched line between his brows never quite disappears. Kevin spots Gino in the doorway and turns back to tell his mother-in-law, "It's a cruel thing to do to you, Francesca. God knows he's just gonna turn around and leave tomorrow."

His mom, her small hands shiny with oil and flecked with carrot skins, turns and sees him. "Well," she says. "Will you? Head out tomorrow?"

"Hey, Ma. Nah. No, I took the week off. Takes abo⊡t a day to get back, though, took a day to get here, so. I can stay a couple days." She looks him up and down, then away just as quickly, and goes back to chopping a lemon. He adds, "Right now there's a break between the last project and this shoreline thing in Maine, I don't know if you've heard about it."

"Real glad you could squeeze us into your busy schedule," Kevin says. "About a year late for the funeral, but it's the thought that counts, right?" He leaves, a heaping bowl of rice under one arm and a pan of lasagna under the other.

For a long minute Gino just watches his mother work. Reaching for this and that. Washing her hands. There's less of her in reality than there had been in his imagination. She tells him the garlic bread is ready, and he falls into the routine of ducking outside to t⊡rn off the gas, grabbing the wire basket off the top of the fridge, a cloth from the drawer on the left, and plucking the steaming slices from the oven pan, folding them under the cloth with the buttery smell of a thousand ancient dinners around the kitchen table. There's a lot of chatter coming from the front room, and someone comes in and out of the back door to bring in the folding chairs that have been rusting out there since before Gino was born.

Gino hovers in the middle of the kitchen. He's spent an inordinate amount of time over the past weeks thinking what he'd say to her. Even in his imagination, he never got it right. Finally, he asks, "Is there anything else to do?"

His mom waves a hand at him without turning around. "Take those out there."

"Okay." And then he tries, "I'm sorry, Ma."

"For what?" She's wiping down the counter now, piling pans and ladles in the sink.

"For. . . ." Gino takes a couple breaths. He's feeling a little sick, which isn't the same as feeling sorry, but is close enough that he's sure it's what he should say. "I should have been here. Last year."

His mom is brisk, businesslike, with her hands. She shakes her head. "You were gone a long time before that. He knew you weren't coming back." She says it plainly, without accusation.

"Right," Gino says. "Okay." He carries the basket of bread into the front room.

Out front there are people everywhere on mismatched chairs, kids cross-legged on the floor, and not enough plates for everyone. A neighbor comes in the door with a package of paper plates to make up the difference. Stevie gestures Gino over to a spot he's saved on the couch, and their mom comes in and settles herself into the big cracked-leather armchair that used to be their dad's. There's a moment where everyone pauses, leaning over their plates. The youngest kid in the room asks if they can eat now and uncle Lenny turns to Gino's mom and says, "Hold up. Francesca? You want to say something?"

She says yes, and puts her plate down on her lap. She'd insisted on taking one of the paper plates. She runs a quick hand over the arm of the chair. It's strange to see her in it. It's strange to see her.

"I hear it's not always easy to get here across the water these days, and it's nice to see you who did." She nods at some folks who Gino didn't know had moved away. "The house is always better with a whole lot of people in it, even if it's a little crowded. Nato and I moved in here a few months before Stevie was born. All the way cross town for an extra bedroom. When we had Eugenio and he wanted his own room, Nato told him, you can make a down payment, then you get your own room." There's some laughter in Gino's direction. His mom turns to her own brother. "And Lenny, you know our dad, God rest him, he didn't like me taking up with Nato, didn't like us moving away from the old neighborhood, and we had some conversations about all that."

Lenny chuckles, incredulous. "That what you wanna call it?"

"Alright," she says. "We had some loud conversations about all that. But then give it ten, twenty years and him and Nato were best goddamn friends, getting up to all sorta trouble together, here in this house. When dad passed, I was a mess. You know what I mean, I wasn't ready for that." She looks at Gino for a moment, then at Stevie. "And your father, he held me up and gave me ways to say goodbye. We did this for my dad, the year after. And if anyone said it was a little strange to have a babang luksa for some old Italian from South Philly, then they had to have a loud conversation with me." She clutches a hand on Lenny's knee. "This year yous've all held me up. So. Let's eat, and say goodbye to Nato."

Kevin and a cousin who Gino can't place take charge of dishing out food. There's a massive salad that he hadn't noticed before, weighted down by a mound of black olives and grated parmesan. The lasagna is meatless, but the pancit bihon has chicken and liver, and there's something that smells like adobo even if it doesn't look like it. Jasmine and Roxie start a fork war over the best-looking corner slice of lasagna, which Kevin settles by taking it for himself. Gino lets mostly everyone be served before him while he tries to unclench his hands and his jaw.

From his left, Lenny shovels all the olives from his own plate onto Gino's, an old joke he'd forgotten they shared. "Good to have you around here," Lenny says.

"Can't get anyone else to take these off your hands?"

"Not all of 'em at once, I gotta do two here, three there, hit five, six plates. It's a logistical nightmare."

"That's rough, man. Lucky I'm a logistics guy."

"Oh yeah? You still with the ah, what's the thing?"

"Army Corps of Engineers, yeah." Gino catches Lenny's searching look. "Almost ten years now," he offers.

Roxie breaks off talking to the neighbor kids and shoots Stevie an accusing look. "Uncle Gino's in the Army?"

"No," Gino answers for her. "Corps' mostly civilians. They do, we do infrastructure projects. Building stuff. They did the levees downtown."

"You worked on that?" Roxie lights up. The levees would have been big news in the city when she was a kid. They're half the reason their little island is still above water.

"No," Kevin says. "He was long gone. But the mail still came then, he sent you postcards from all his little projects. When was the levee, what year was that, hm?" Roxie looks uncomfortable, but Jasmine puts in that she was in sixth grade. "Right! Big year. You were in that inter-city youth boxing thing, Jas. She made the quarter finals. Where were you that time, Eugenio?"

Gino isn't sure what year Jasmine was in the sixth grade, or exactly how old she is now, but he can see Kevin waiting for him to ask. "Connecticut," he says. "Coastal restoration."

"Oh, yeah? How'd that work out for Connecticut?"

"C'mon, Kev," says Stevie.

Gino says, "Not bad, last I heard. I've seen worse."

"Yeah, me too," Lenny says, and jerks his chin at the front window. Everyone laughs. Gino nods, which is close enough to laughing.

Another neighbor, a big guy whose name Gino can't come up with, asks, "Yous guys got work planned down here?" And the woman next to him, his wife maybe, says, "Oh, they should put up boardwalks!" And somebody else, "We've been saying, there's plenty of high enough ground for boardwalks to connect up to downtown. They gonna do that, Gino?"

"They don't really tell me that kind of thing. I just keep the truck and everything running. I'm a, you know what I mean, a glorified mechanic." He trails off, and his brother laughs.

"Please," Stevie says. "They're not gonna do shit. I mean, sorry, but you're not, right? The levee was what, eight years back, and nothing since that. They gave up."

Francesca, who had been quiet, eating, says, "They did. But that's okay. Everyone is allowed to give up when they gotta." From the tension in the room, it's not a popular statement, but nobody argues her on it.

After a second, someone brings up the NBA finals, and how pissed Nato would have been that the Raptors made it this far again. And then his general grudge against Canadian teams in the NBA, and then his earnest incompetence on the court himself, as a young man. And then a picture is brought out of a shoebox, and it's Gino, perhaps three years old, with a bowl cut and a look of childish ecstasy, up on his father's shoulders, his father's hands holding Gino's chubby child-legs, Gino's arms up at the end of an arc, a basketball in the air, suspended in the moment before it fell short of the net.

Gino ducks out to sit on the front stoop and finds a pack of Stevie's cigarettes where he's always left them, in the nook of a broken corner of the top step. He lights one just as the screen door creaks open and shut and his brother sucks his teeth at him and says, "Hey, asshole." Gino hands him the one he's lit and takes another for himself. They settle into their old arrangement, Gino facing the street on the middle step, Stevie behind him, leaning back against the railing, between the two of them a view of the narrow street and the intersection nearby, and of all the folks who would wander over to shoot the shit. Nobody wandering today, just the distant figures of other stoop-loiterers at another house. A familiar view, but uncanny.

"It's so quiet around here," Gino says. "It's weird."

"It's been this quiet for, hell . . . years. You just weren't around to notice."

Gino grimaces, shakes his head. "I'm not gonna keep apologizing for living my own life."

"Didn't ask you to, I'm just saying."

"Right. Sorry. Shouldn't put words in your mouth."

Stevie, never one to let discomfort sit for long, asks Gino how work is. "And you still seeing that girl? Tina? Trisha?"

"Tonya," says Gino. "We called it quits. It's the job. I'm somewhere for six, eight months, then a couple weeks of nothing, being a bum on her couch, then some other place, do it all over again. I like the work. Get a project, see it through, tie it up, I like that. But I think she got sick of the whole thing."

"Condolences, man."

"Nah, I'm good."

"So whose couch you bumming on between projects now?" Stevie asks. Gino shrugs.

"Just around, really. HQ has some temp housing, so I'm there mostly."

"Bro, hold up, are you homeless right now?"

Gino shoves back against Stevie's knee. "Fuck off, man, I don't need a place is all."

"Alright, alright! I was gonna say you could crash here, but being honest, I think I'd have a heart attack if you said yes."

"And Kevin would fuckin' kill you. Or me."

Stevie grunts an agreement. "You wouldn't stand a chance. He's a biter, too."

Gino sputters. "Come on, man, I don't need to know that shit." He hesitates, then says, "You guys don't have to stay here either, you know."

"Gino . . . ."

"Just saying, I know what it's like to feel trapped here, but you're not. You don't have to stick around and watch it all sink, you know, I can help, we can pack up Ma, and . . . ."

Stevie cuts him off. "Come the fuck on, man. You think Ma's leaving this house? You wanna pry her out with a crowbar? You're gonna break her heart with that, and who's gonna take care of her then, you?"

"I could help you get set up somewhere."

"Get the fuck outta here with that, come on."

"I'm just saying," he says.

"I know what you're saying. But be real, okay. Ma's not going anywhere. And if Kevin and I leave, there's no one to be with Ma—you're not dropping everything and coming back. So yeah, you're not trapped, because I am. And that's not on you, I'm glad you're out there doing your thing. You're my little brother, you know, you're a smart kid."

"Stevie, I'm thirty-six."

"See? You can count real high and everything." Stevie laughs at his own joke. That loud, unselfconscious snorting that always makes Gino smile. "Jesus, listen to us. Like we're in therapy or some shit."

"I am, actually," Gino offers.

"For real?"

"Yeah." Stevie nudges Gino's back with his foot, so he goes on. "Work has these folks on staff, and it's free, so I figured might as well, y'know what I mean."

"Huh. Nice of them, I guess. So what do yous talk about?" Gino cranes his neck around to glare at him. "What? I've never been to therapy before, I'm curious, come on."

"It's personal."

"Alright, fine, don't tell me anything."

"It's like AA, you know, it's confidential."

"How much confidential shit can you even have?"

"Aw c'mon, screw you, Stevie."

He laughs again. "Kidding, I'm kidding."

Gino finishes his cigarette and rummages in the pack for another. Offers Stevie one, lights them both. Overhead, the sun is behind gray clouds, and some sort of hawk or kite is making high, irregular circles. "He's cool, the therapist they got," Gino says. "He thought coming here for this was a good idea. He's kind of a hardass, though, you know. Calls me on my bullshit."

"That's a big job, you're full of bullshit."

"Hilarious."

"I know, right?" Stevie taps a little song on the top step with his fingertips. Inside the house, Roxie and Kevin are talking fast, back and forth, loud and happy enough. "So, go on," Stevie says. "What kind of bullshit?"

Gino sighs. He gestures with his chin back at the front door. "This kind, mostly. First session we had, he gave it fifteen minutes before asking why I kept getting angry at myself for having feelings."

"Oh, fuck."

"Yeah. I almost walked out and he was like, see? Right there, there it is again." He shakes his head, smiles. "Bastard."

"You still do that, though," Stevie says, with all the self-assurance of someone who'd changed his diapers.

"I do. But I notice it now, which he says is good."

Stevie blows smoke out the corner of his mouth and they watch the hawk drop out of sight somewhere over the marsh. “Is it? Good?”

“Nah, it sucks. Now I get angry about being angry.”

Stevie laughs so hard that both his daughters and his husband bang out through the front door to see what they’re missing, the three of them fitting themselves into Gino and Stevie’s stoop arrangement in a new config□ration that makes him feel crowded, but at least not crowded out. The kids surround him on the steps, long teenage limbs getting everywhere. Kevin even offers him a bite of the slice of pie he carried out with him, and barely makes a face when Gino uses his fork.

Gino walks with his mom to his dad’s grave, abo□t a five min□te trip up the street. It was Kevin who pointedly herded his family and everyone else left at the house to clean things up and follow along afterwards, so Gino and his mom are alone together for the time being in the dim late afternoon, walking through sticky air and the droning noise of a neighbor’s household generator. It’s slow going, not beca□se of any infirmity on Francesca’s part, b□t beca□se she walks slowly, and always has. An infuriating trait in a city person, finally at home now that this part of the city has been c□t off, made circumstantially provincial. Gino doesn’t mind meandering, but he’s not used to the sound of his mother not talking.

“Stevie’s girls look all grown up,” he says. She nods. She puts her hand on his arm and he folds it so her hand is tucked in the crook of his elbow and they walk like that, a dignified little procession.

“He’s a good father,” she says. “You still not seeing anyone?”

“Nah.”

“Would you tell me if you were?”

Gino ducks his head. “Probably.”

They come to the graveyard. Stevie had written to Gino about the place, and sent some pictures, but it’s more odd, more abrupt, to see it in person. What used to be a messy, six-way intersection in the middle of the neighborhood had become just so much useless space when the seasonal flooding stopped being seasonal, and residents were cut off from the closest gas station, now half an hour away over the water. Folks brought out the sledgehammers and tore it down to dirt. The original plan had been to till the soil and put in vegetable crops, but before they started planting, someone on 23rd St died, and all at once the residents of the newborn island realized they didn't know what to do with their dead.

Cemeteries in South Philly had been exhumed and relocated long ago, well before most of the living started to leave. If the bereaved were so inclined, and could afford it, they'd ship their dead up to a plot in the northwest of the city, or even to the suburbs. Churches and mosques and synagogues pitched in, but most people, if their faith allowed, opted for cremation. The shore had been in flux their whole lives, and there was no assurance their kids wouldn't have to dig up grandpa and ship his bones even further inland a couple decades down the line. Unfortunately for the remains of West Passyunk, however, when the water rose around them, no crematoriums remained on dry land. So they had the body of a young woman whose heart gave out, and a fresh field of open dirt. They planted her in it. And then the next death, and the next one. By the time Gino's dad was buried here, he had plenty of company.

The graveyard has the long triangular shape of the old intersection, enclosed by a chain-link fence to keep out dogs and raccoons. The grass is clipped short, the regular sort of lawn grass instead of the mess of marsh grasses that have crept in everywhere else. White forget-me-nots are dotted in among the plots, and one corner of the yard is taken up by a huge mess of purple aster. The markers are pale wood, names and dates burned into them in a dark, neat script. Gino's mom leads him to his dad's plot, which is catching some late light.

Gino knows his father is dead. He's known it for a year, but seeing a grave with his father's name on it feels like coming down off a high wire—sickening, and sudden. He sits down in the grass, and after wiping some dust and grit off the marker, his mom sits down next to him.

"You should come visit him in the morning, too," she says. "A lot of bees then, and bluebirds. I almost moved that feeder over here, the one he put out by the back door. But then they wouldn't come to the house so much, and they come here already anyhow."

Gino doesn't trust himself to speak yet. He hadn't known it

would feel like this. He had hoped to avoid feeling like this, indefinitely. The finality of it, and the premonition that she would be gone soon enough too, and even Stevie one day, and that this gentle garden of the dead would flood with saltwater, and he wouldn't get another chance to be brave enough to stick around. He thought he'd buried them for himself already by leaving, by not watching it happen. But they're still here, and all he'd done was lose time that he'll never recover, and let Stevie dig their dad's grave all on his own. Gino's squeezing his hands, one in the other, and his mom rests hers on top of them, a question. He shakes his head convulsively. "It's fine, sorry. I'm fine, sorry, I'm sorry."

"Alright," she says. She squeezes his hand, rubs his back. "Alright, you go on."

He knows what Stevie said, but he's gotta ask, it's clawing at him. "You and all them could come back with me," Gino says. "I can take some more time off and find a place, doesn't have to be that far, there's a whole lot of Pennsylvania. We can get you outta here, it's time to get outta here."

"All of us?" She looks at him like he just spat in her face. "Your brother can make his own decisions. And you, baby boy I'm happy to see your face, but you can go anytime." She nods at the grave. "But I'm not about to leave him. Don't you ask me to."

"I'm sorry, Ma." For leaving, for coming back. For the moment a few days from now when he'll leave again.

"That's alright. It's alright to have things you're sorry for. Your dad lived a good long life, and he left still sorry for all sorts of things. You go on, be sorry. That's okay."

A trio of swallows have landed on the fence and are calling their clear, tittering trills into the dusk. Insects are flitting around, and the birds take turns launching themselves from the fence, diving in wild arcs, then coming back to rest. The other two waiting, chirrup-laughing, the insects droning on, oblivious to the game that's been made of their fate.

"I couldn't watch," Gino says, leaning into his mom's hand on his back. "I couldn't watch it happen. Dad, the neighborhood."

Her hand stills, then she pats him briskly, and stands. Stevie, Kevin, and the girls are coming through the gate and into the yard, chattering like birds. "Well, anytime you want to see us, we'll be here," his mom says. "Whether you're watching or not."

Nicasio Andres Reed is a writer, poet, and essayist whose work has appeared in venues such as *Strange Horizons*, *Shimmer*, *Lightspeed*, and *Fireside*. He spent a long span of his itinerant childhood in Philadelphia, and now lives in Tagaytay, in the Philippines, with four dogs, some family, and the occasional uninvited monitor lizard. Find him on Twitter @nicasioreed or at nicasioreed.com.

Gills

Nicholas Clute

“You hear about those people putting gills in their necks?”

“Yeah.”

“It won’t let you live underwater, y’know, like a fish, but it gives you a bit of time. Lets you stay down longer.”

“Yeah.”

“Man, I’d kill for some gills sometimes. Remember when I got my arm stuck? I could’ve had time to get free on my own, wouldn’t have gone loopy. Wouldn’t have needed you there.”

“They let you talk underwater too?”

“Shut up, man, just keep rowing.”

Two brothers of unequal age sat across from each other in a small wooden boat. Young was just a boy, fragile, and animated. Allas was quiet, his body sunburned and broad. They paddled across the choppy bay from Oakland to the remains of San Francisco. It was difficult, rowing into the wind.

“It also shows you’re a diver, y’know?” Young continued. “Like, everyone knows you don’t just muck around the swamps for pitch, you dive. If I had cash I’d get gills. I’ll probably get a tattoo instead, on my neck like the real thing. You thought about getting a tattoo?”

“I don’t need to show off like that.”

“Whatever, man, I know plenty of people who got them.”

“Like who?” asked Allas.

“Jere does.”

“Him? You know why he has money, right?”

“So what? He’s living big.”

Allas laughed. “What’s he doing running around with you then?”

“Fuck you, we go way back.” Young scowled. “One day, I’ll live big.”

Allas pulled up the oars for a moment, seawater sparkling as it dripped down their length and dropped into the boat. The beige hills of Oakland rose above the bay, throwing shadows in the morning light. Heat was already radiating off the water, and he could feel the wind blowing them backwards. "Hey, you know I was joking."

"Whatever. I'm not gonna keep diving for this shit forever."

Young stood up, snatched the oars, and pushed Allas aside to take his seat rowing. He nearly upset the boat in the process. They continued in silence. The windswept archipelago grew nearer, and they could make out shattered cars, tangled telephone wires, and the rust-streaked decay of abandoned buildings. It was beautiful in a brutal way, those scraps of the city not yet claimed by the rising tide.

"What'll you do when you're rich?" Allas asked. They stood and swapped oars again.

"I dunno, man, I'ma leave this shitty work, leave Oakland, y'know? Get myself a place up high, that looks over the Bay, looks over the City," Young waved his hands at everything that lay in front of him, excited. "Maybe somewhere towers don't block the sunset. Somewhere I can relax in a big ass bed and look down at everyone below me."

Allas clenched his jaw. He and Pa would always be afterthoughts. Even in Young's dreams, family was ballast that held him down.

"The normal spot or somewhere new?" Allas asked.

Young pulled a coin from the bag at his waist. "Tops is our normal place," he said, tossing it up, then snatching it out of the air. He opened his hand, revealing a worn face. "Tops."

They rowed around the largest island, toward their lucky bay, but there was another boat there already. It was small, delicate, with thin sides and shiny paint. Nothing like their peeling craft. A man in a black wets□it fiddled with an oxygen tank, preparing to dive.

"Hiya!" Young chirped. "Can we share the water?"

There was no response. Allas rowed closer.

"Hey mister, do yo□ mind . . . ." B□t the diver c□t Yo□ng off.

"You don't have an anchor, do you? Get the hell outta here, you're gonna crash into me."

Allas turned their boat so he faced the diver.

"There's plenty of water here for all of us," he said, gesturing at the placid bay. "We'll be caref□l . . . ." B□t the diver started sho□ting.

"Did you hear me, jackass? Are you dumb, or am I gonna have to make you go?"

The man reached behind the gunwale and lifted up a sleek

speargun. Allas pulled their boat away as fast as he could; a hiss passed their bow as the spear splashed nearby. The most direct retreat led them closer to the unprotected mouth of the bay.

"Hey, hey we're getting near the open. . . ." Young said, anxious.

"Not now."

They rowed into the hot wind. Salt spray scratched their throats and whipped their eyes, but Allas kept a course around the outer point. Soon they found themselves in a narrow passage between two jagged rock islands that only gave minimal protection.

"Current's too strong to float," he said. "We'll have to paddle the boat in place."

"Is it worth it?" replied Young, unsure.

"You know the deal."

Young nodded, reassuring himself. "Tops we leave." He flipped the coin; a sudden gust of wind took the coin, and his brother lunged to save it from going overboard.

Allas opened his hand. "I'll dive first."

He pulled off his shirt, flexed his broad shoulders, and strapped a short knife to his ankle. He breathed deep, exhaling more fully each time. Releasing air, he began to hum, a noise that was halfway between a meditative mantra and a death rattle.

He was a good diver—even without oxygen tanks, he could stay underwater for five minutes, almost six if he didn't exert himself. He stood up, eyes placid, bumped his brother's fist, and then back-flipped into the water with a smooth motion. Young hooted at the spectacle, pulling on the oars to fight the wind.

The water was cool but not unpleasant. Allas swam deeper, getting his bearings: a decrepit slide and jungle gym poked through ribbons of kelp down below. Buildings shouldn't be too far away. He kicked until he saw a wide boulevard, lined with the sagging shells of once ornate buildings, their trim rotted by salt water.

All of this was a bad sign; it usually grew along old industrial areas where it could leach contaminants, not the residential parts of town. He surfaced.

"I dunno if it's any good here, we're in the fancy part. There's a playground," said Allas.

"I'll try some side streets, look for a warehouse."

They swapped places and Young dove down. Allas rowed to

keep the boat between the only landmarks he could see, the crumbling spire of the cathedral on the east island and an old power pole atop jagged cliffs to the west.

Young was down for a long time. Just as Allas began to worry, his brother s□rfaced, hands filled with a silver sl□dge, flecked with turquoise. Glitterpitch.

"Damn, is that real?"

The power plants paid handsomely for the st□ff, a fissile biomaterial with a twelve-syllable name. But to divers, it was sticky silver gunk they called glitterpitch. Nobody knew exactly how or where it grew. Most people tramped through the marshes of Oakland, gleaning bits of it at a time.

There had to be something wrong—the pitch Young gathered looked pure, and he held more in his hands than they could hope to collect in a day, even a week.

"Go down, it's crazy," Young gasped. "It's blooming."

Allas looked at him with a blank expression, unclear.

"Behind the buildings east of the big street. Third one down has a busted roof, it's all up in there."

Allas pulled his brother into the boat, and helped scrape the silver mess into a tub. They'd never needed this much space for the pitch, they would have to be creative to bring it all back. He took a deep breath and dove down again.

Passing the playground and the boulevard, Allas kicked along the surface of the streets, looking for the signs of pitch. He swam upwards, over the roofs of the buildings, until he saw a great skylight, shattered long ago. The kelp-rimed opening led into a dim grotto. He p□shed himself thro□gh, down to the remains of the third floor.

He was overwhelmed by uncanny as he swam around a living room forty feet underwater. A family of crabs had taken residence in one corner, and a built-in bench by the ruined bay window was covered in oyster shells. Allas sat down, staring at the room.

People had lived here, never knowing their house would one day be submerged. What had it been like, living through the rise? Waves lapping the street and steps, wetting the books propped under the kitchen table to keep it level, washing away the patched quilts on their bed. Slowly but forever rising, squeezing everything away.

It was okay, though, the sea was done rising. He and his

brother and their father were safe enough in their house across the bay and up the hills. The house that was so unlike the one he sat in now; for one, their house wasn't covered in glitterpitch, soft, oily silver mounds shimmering with turquoise. Its glimmer danced as you looked at it, twirling in the light as if it were alive.

How long had he been down? He was getting loopy, he realized with a start. He jammed fistf□ls of glitterpitch into a pocket, and p□shed off toward the s□rface, tendrils of t□rq□oise and silver spiraling off his bare feet.

It took him several minutes to regain his breath once he was back, Young pounding his back.

"There's.... There's so m□ch. Where did it come from? There's no.... The growth?"

His brother understood. "It's just going crazy there, what's it feeding on?"

"Maybe we've got it wrong," Allas said, recovering. "Maybe polluted places don't grow it best, maybe they just grow it slowest. We find it there before it b□rns o□t and dissipates."

They were eager to harvest. Young clipped a small bag to his waist before diving in. Most days he filled it with shellfish, knick knacks, remnants of the old city he fo□nd along the seafloor: detrit□s. Today, they wo□ld fill all the space they co□ld afford.

Allas stayed in the boat, struggling to keep it still. The winds whistled through the strait, making it almost as much work above as it was below. At least up here he could breathe.

His brother surfaced a few meters away, and Allas rowed over. Helping him over the side of the boat, his jaw dropped. He knew the bloom was large, but Young's thin body was covered in silver pitch. It coated his long dark eyelashes, cl□ng to his short fingernails; every inch of the boy's skin was plastered, and lugubrious drips of opalescent oil slowly slid down his face. He didn't even bother to scrape off the precio□s sl□dge, simply □pending his bag into the t□b. It contained no sand or silt, no fish bones or r□bble. They were splattered in wealth.

The brothers dove, frantic at first, b□t as the day wore on they slowed to take their time. The sun shone down, kissing their arms and legs as they took their turns, diving and rowing.

"What are we gonna do with all of it?" Young asked as they

ate lunch. "What do you think it's worth? It's gotta be worth more 'cause it's pure?"

"I don't know."

"Y'know, I'm gonna do it. I'ma get those gills."

"Yeah?"

"We get rich from diving, I wanna do something that honors that, y'know?"

Allas laughed and nodded, tilting his head back and closing his eyes. He stretched an arm out, trails of silver swirling off where his knuckles brushed the water.

"I'll get nicer shoes too," Young continued. "Something that lasts longer than the shit I got back home. I'm sick of feeling every goddamn step I take, y'know?"

Allas' smile faltered. Young hadn't been able to dive with him until recently. After their father's accident, he'd been the only one making money for the family. It had never been enough. Even with both boys diving, they barely scraped by.

"And I'ma buy us another boat," continued Young, not noticing his brother's melancholy. "A bigger one so we can pay people to dive for us. Think about that, being a captain, being in charge. I'll get one of those fancy boats you can sleep on.

"But you know what, I think I'ma do something none of us ever done, I'm gonna go all the way up north, see what that's like. They don't have to buy water, I hear. Crazy. I hear it gets cold up there, that it actually rains. I don't know anyone who's been to another country."

Allas sighed quietly. Their dreams had just become reality, and he still wasn't a part of his brother's future.

"What'll you do?" Young asked, suddenly looking back.

"I've never really thought about it," said Allas. "Yeah, I guess we would start a fleet."

The small boy nodded eagerly, drinking in the future with abandon.

"And I think I'd get us a new house, something bigger and more comfortable. Not too far away from the neighborhood, I know Dad likes it there. But somewhere we don't need bars on the windows. Somewhere with a deck. We could sit out back, watch the sun set, and just be happy there. Be a family."

He never allowed himself to dream like this, and was unsettled by how easily these plans poured from his mouth. Now that they were rich.

Allas continued, "Even if it takes all the money we get from this, we'll get Dad some new legs, y'know? I haven't seen him run in years. He used to love that, the days he didn't dive he'd wake up early and just run. Up and down the hills, along the shore as the sun came up. Before the city was awake, he'd always say. He used to do that to clear his head. Before . . . you know, before all that he used to love running. We can get him fixed now."

"Man, why don't you ever want anything for yourself?" Young's smooth face had darkened into ugly resentment. "It's always what you'd do for me, for Dad. It's never about you."

Allas considered this for a moment. "I want you to be happy, Dad to be happy. I dunno, that's what I want." He sat up, pulled the oars a few strokes to reposition them, then laid them back down.

"I just wanted to have this one day to feel good, y'know," said Young, raising his voice. "To have some actual happy thoughts about the future. This is the first time I haven't had to spin bullshit, make everything seem okay.

"You're always so fucking happy all the time, so good at putting on the right face, saying the right thing, doing the right thing. It's so goddamn exhausting, and I'm tired. I'm tired of you being perfect, always being the role model and me being the fuckup. No, don't act like I don't know. I see how y'all look at me."

"Hey, I didn't mean . . . ."

"You didn't mean what?" Young cut in. "To always be right? To always be better? You could be going places with your life, but you're gonna help the family, no matter what it costs you.

"Fuck. I wish I was you. What is it I'm missing? I can't even be mad at you because you're always doing the right thing. Won't you just get pissed or be selfish, just once? For me?"

They sat in silence. A new wind blew, sudden chill biting at their arms. Allas reached for the oars, but his brother pushed him back, firm, aggressive.

"Fuck, off, I can do this. You paddled us out here. Like always."

Young piloted them back into the middle of the channel and they finished their lunch to make room for more pitch. Eventually Young broke the silence.

"Look, this sucks. I don't have a reason to hate you. You're everything to me. I can't hate yo□, so I need to fig□re o□t how to not hate myself, I guess."

Tears cut streaks through the salt and pitch that stained Young's face.

"It's not easy," said Allas, his voice breaking. "It's not. And I'm not perfect, no matter what you think. You're good at forgetting when I mess up. You're real good at that.

"You're not a screwup, man. You're young, you're learning. You don't know how proud of you Dad and I are. We don't tell you that enough."

Young wiped his face, smearing his tears.

"You're right to dream bigger than me," said Allas. "There's nothing wrong with dreaming big, but you gotta dream big enough for the both of us. Because you know I'm no good at it."

They both sat there for a minute, eyes cast downward.

"I'm gonna go down again." Yo□ng said, sniffing. "Get the rest of what's there."

He reached for Allas' sho□lder, gentle and firm; the two shared their gaze for a moment, then Young dove overboard, leaving him rocking and alone adrift with the wind.

They scooped up treasure and kept their boat from the rocks. The s□n lowered in the sky, and they filled their boat with pitch. Young was underwater when Allas saw the new shiny boat round the corner, the solo diver headed towards them. They kept their distance and continued to dive.

Young's head broke the surface in a frenzy.

"He's stuck, he's down there, he got stuck!" Young wheezed, sucking air into his lungs.

"What are you talking about?"

"The other g□y, the other diver. He was trying to find o□r bloom, and he got stuck in a car down there!"

"Can you help him?"

"I tried, I need your help!"

"We'll crash!" said Allas, motioning to the cliffs.

Young let out a pained cry, and dove below the surface.

Allas rowed the boat in a circle, nervous thoughts racing through his head. What could he do? Leave the boat to crash, all for a man who had tried to kill them earlier?

Young's head broke the waves again, more frantic than before.

"His leg's stuck, man, he's drowning! I need you, now!"

"What am I supposed to do?" Allas shouted.

Young stared at him, saying nothing, then dove down again. His silence was worse than words. Their earlier conversation echoed in his head.

You're always doing the right thing.

Allas let out an anguished yell and dove into the waves.

Below the surface, the afternoon sun had turned the old city into a forest of cerulean shadow. He kicked down to the street level and looked for his brother. Near the building with their bloom he spotted his brother swimming in circles around the pitted carcass of a car, a flood of b□bbles er□pting from the far side.

The diver had somehow trapped his leg in the door and severed a breathing line on the jagged metal. The man was trapped and drowning. Allas motioned to the diver to relax, and to his brother to help him. The diver made incomprehensible signals, grabbing at Allas' shoulders as if he were drunk. They needed to act fast.

On the sidewalk, there was a long metal tube covered in barnacles; the fallen remnant of a street sign. It took them both, but they swam the pole over to the car and pried it against the door. The jaws snapped open, and the diver's leg was freed. Both brothers p□shed off toward the s□rface, b□t the man was not following. He stayed near the car, hips and legs flailing.

Allas motioned for his brother to ascend, and then dove back down, wrapping his long arms around the diver. The man wouldn't budge, his weight belt caught on something. Frantic, Allas pulled the knife from his ankle and cut any strap he could grasp, slashing the man free. The diver thrashed, and they slammed into a raw metal edge of the car; a bloom of red erupted from the boy's arm. It would be okay, he thought, the diver was loose. He held him tight, and together they swam toward the dark reflection of the s□rface.

Allas tried to pull himself upward, but his arm refused commands, floating by his side. He kicked harder, the soles of his feet tickled by the rush of air escaping the diver's tank they'd left down below. It was strange, he realized, that he should feel like this,

his lungs on fire for want of air when he was surrounded by perfect, breathable bubbles. He opened his mouth, reaching to swallow one, but it darted out of his reach and upward. He kept going, following that bubble's rise, but the surface seemed so far away, and he was very tired of swimming. How long had he been underwater? The math was simple: several years of diving, twenty dives a day (usually), five minutes a dive (give or take), that makes almost a thousand days spent underwater. No, five hundred. Wait, hours, not days. Divide that by twenty-four . . . . How old was he now, had he spent most of his life underwater? Surrounded by water, at least. It followed him wherever he went, from the steam lifting off his coffee each morning to the clouds that passed overhead, their moisture just out of reach. When he was young his mother used to take him to the docks to watch the great tankers pull into harbor, metal-bellied leviathans, each unloading over a trillion liters of Chinese freshwater into the city tanks so that Oakland could drink and bathe and grow plants on their balconies and rooftops and community gardens, trillions of liters of water from each of the ships and yet they were nothing but drops compared to the vastness of ocean upon which he floated. His head swam with numbers, mathematics looping through his mind and tumbling around him as a million porcelain bubbles passed before his eyes. He hadn't thought of his mom in a long time.

They shattered the mirrored surface and he released his grip on the diver. His head was above water, but he could not inhale. His small, fragile brother swam over to him, shouting or maybe mumbling, but he did not notice because he was calmly drifting on his back, captivated by the sky which was painted in streaks, orange and purple blending together at the margins, the colors pulsing with the slowing beat of his heart. It was peaceful, the world a beautiful blur whose edges faded to blank perfection.

With a sudden rush, purple clouds and orange sunset snapped into focus. He gasped. He could hear his own breath, his heart pounding in his ears, his brother shouting at him. The volume of the world had been turned back up and it was excruciating.

"He's breathing, it's okay man, we're okay," Young was shouting, holding the other diver in a rescue position while treading water. He jerked his head to the island to the east, where the remains of a road slumped into the sea. "We just gotta get to that little beach over there, okay?" Allas assented without words.

As they dragged themselves onto the small patch of ground, he looked back at the channel. The boats had crashed; their small and sturdy craft sliced through the thin skin of the other, and both were leaking. Clinging together like doomed lovers, the boats turned languid circles, drifting inexorably across the channel toward the jagged cliffs.

Young laid the diver down on the gravel and began to run back into the water, but with his good arm Allas pulled him out of the s□rf and into a tight embrace. They str□ggled at first, b□t exhausted and injured, they soon held each other still.

The brothers stood there, warm wind drying the water on their faces, as they watched the boats throw themselves against the rocks. The hulls were soon splintered and ripped, and from those gashes bled oily silver m□d, t□rq□oise flecks glowing in the setting sun.

The nicer boat lay strewn across the rocks like discarded rubbish. Their small craft, everything they had in this world, bobbed on the surface for a moment that seemed to last forever, then slipped below the seafoam.

They carried the limp diver along a road up the island, shattered asphalt biting their bare feet. Atop were the remains of an old cathedral, a great grey shell that once loomed over the city. It was r□ined, b□t it wo□ld shelter them for the night. They sh□ffled through a great arched doorway and laid the diver to recover on the low stone altar.

The brothers sat in the second row of cold pews. Behind them the sun burned away as always, from yellow to peach to twilight. Before them was a hole in the structure, yawning nothing where the sacristy once stood. They watched their shadows lengthen, blend into dusk as the sun passed away. Through the void in the church was the city, their city, individual lights winking on as night approached. Wind whistled through the husk of this sacred place. Young turned to his brother, who was leaned forward as if in prayer.

"They'll come looking for him, right?"

Allas did not answer.

"And they'll pick □s □p too. And then we'll find that again, won't we? I bet we can. Now we know how it blooms, we can find another, right? I know we will. We can come out here again, real soon. Once your arm's better."

Allas sat there with his eyes closed, head resting on the pew in front of them, arm limp at his side. It did not hurt. It did not feel much at all.

He looked at the diver drying upon the altar. A small beacon strapped to his ankle was blinking, a slow pulse of reassurance. Rescue would come, eventually. Allas turned to his brother, the small boy whose eyes burned fierce with hope.

Allas nodded once, then nodded again, and put his good arm around Young, pulling him close. "Yeah. We'll find it again."

Young leaned into his brother's shoulder, relaxing into that steadfast warmth. They sat there for a long time, together, while around them the day evaporated and quietly condensed into night.

Nicholas Clute used to be a biologist in the Bay Area, but now lives in the mountains. He's still a biologist.

water-logged roots

Cislyn Smith

after the storm
there is a dryad on my roof
and the river is licking the porch
like it can taste freedom in the foundation
got news for you, bayou baby,
there's only things to hold you back in there
best look elsewhere for escape.
I splash out to take a better look
and the tree tells me to be careful of fire ants
floating spheres of pain
surrounding the precious queen in the middle
ready to swarm.
Well, I'm not impressed with that.
We're all trying to protect something
(aren't we?)
and we'll sting to do so if it comes down to it.
Besides, I've got on my granddaddy's waders
they still smell like fish and stale cigarette smoke
though he's been gone twelve years now
if the reek of memories won't keep the biting things back
maybe his ghost will.
My granddaddy didn't care about flood or fire
he set the lawn ablaze once with a careless butt
smoke and flame carried on the wind of dryer days
but that's long passed now
and I'm past the washed-out gravel driveway
looking back
at the combination of oak and house
thinking sweaty chainsaw thoughts
though she looks so pretty up there
such a jaunty angle
crowning the house with leaves
She says she don't care what I do,
being uprooted makes her cavalier like that

but maybe I care.
I slap a mosq□ito off my arm
and consider the smear of blood there
thicker than water, they say
though I never did know what density has to do with it
so little floats in this brackish mess
but underneath the oak branches
in the broken eggshell attic
are baby books, old military uniforms
fishing poles, holiday ornaments
yearbooks nibbled by silverfish
all being caressed by the dryad's twiggy fingers.
Right then
with the sun slanting through the clouds
and mud churning around boots
my heart whispers
let the beetles have it
let the gators sleep like logs in front of the tv
and eat defrosted frozen meals
let the sandhill cranes stalk through the living room
and the bedrooms fill with black mold
eating baby blankets and pillows and teddy bears
spreading like gravy stains on the thanksgiving dinner linens
I'm done protecting this st□ff
and ready to p□t me at the center
swarming for dryer land and better places
there's a car in the garage
gassed up, right next to the mower
ready to go
I don't care about water getting in
I just want to get out
little metal ants are marching down the interstate
back into the state they fled
ready for reconstruction
clogging the roadways south
while my eye turns north
just like the storm did
considering deconstruction instead
right now

this moment
the getting is good
let's go

Cislyn Smith (she/her) likes playing pretend, playing games, and playing with words. She grew up in Florida but calls Madison, Wisconsin her home now. She has been known to crochet tentacles, write stories at odd hours, and study stone dead languages. She is occasionally dismayed by the lack of secret passages in her house. Cislyn's poems and stories have appeared in *Strange Horizons*, *Diabolical Plots*, and *Daily Science Fiction*, among other places. She is a first reader for *Uncanny Magazine* and *Giganotosaurus*, a graduate of the Viable Paradise Workshop, and one of the founding members of the Dream Foundry.

When someone says the world is a fish

Nancy Lynée Woo

Someone has left the building. The building is now
a r□bble of bones. B□tterflies are sometimes kisses,
but mostly larvae. Language: a cocoon to emerge into.

To come down from the tree means breaking
a bough. Rocking to wake. The world is a nursery
and rhymes are waves. To be a person describing

is to be a rat scavenging at the crumbs of language
for the remains of thought. Holiness has nothing
to do with it. Yet, meringue. Yet, music.

Yet, everything. In other words, divinity is a shoebox
at a science fair for the other words. I am not sure
my words are my own. I walk past a bookshelf

and read *How Nature Works*. I read how nature works
in the spinning of a silk worm. Someone reads out loud,
"How nature works." To be awake in the world

means to be aware of sleeping. I won't survive language.
Language is the only way to survive. Thank goddess,
I was never given a god to flo□nder for. A man with a tie

can be an instrument of violence. Why not say so?
For fear of being locked up, we keep our wisteria
to ourselves. I am bursting dragonfruit, pulling cards

and reading. The definition of "apocalypse" is "to reveal."
So what if my language is pleased with itself?
To speak at all has been a travail. I am cacophonous

now, a body of scales dragging along the sand.
Don't mind me while I feast on oil fumes.
How are we still manufacturing plastic foam?

Even fairies need to breathe. The slot machine
dings. Any money I get needs to be cleansed.
Who has the power to move the currency of thought?

Whose hook is in my cheek? I eat puzzles for lunch.
A bomb goes off in a break room. If the poem is a vine,
the climbing to where becomes the question.

Nancy Lynée Woo is a poet, educator, and community organizer. As a 2022 Artists at Work fellow, she brings arts programming to community gardens. Previously, she has received fellowships from PEN America, Arts Council for Long Beach, and Idyllwild Writers Week. Nancy has an MFA in poetry from Antioch University and a BA in sociology from UC Santa Cr□z and. Find her cavorting aro□nd Long Beach (Tongva), California, and online at nancylyneewoo.com or @fancifulnance on social.

Heat

Tim Fab-Eme

I understand you don't like talking sex and indoor games
when the Sun is high and the winds take on
the warmth of a kiss. Everything takes the extreme nowadays;
it's no longer the luxury of race, religion, and politics.
But I'm bored because there's nothing else to talk about
when the heat is high and my lips crave yours.

Our kids are in school learning new ways to take
more from the world. Do you wonder what life would
be in a cent⊡ry or two? There'll be fires, floods,
droughts, and pandemics . . . oh, I forgot, you dread bad news.
You think there'll be more love if we hope more.

We walk around and talk about paradise whenever we want;
I try to laugh loud more every time my mind
wanders away from the lair of a world beyond love.
But the heat is on and I've got no way

of looking away from sex, and the heat is much
and we're afraid our bodies would rain heavily again
and the bed would be soaked and you don't like that.

So, we sit out under the almond fanning our faces,
giggling the way foes feign smiles, thinking more of heaven

than what we feel now and will ever have. Earth.

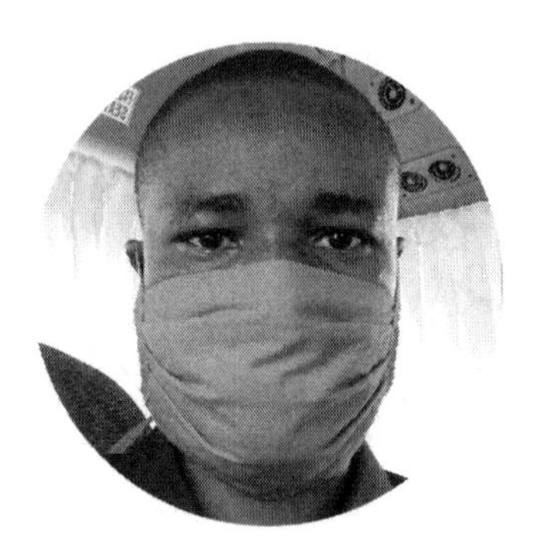

Tim Fab-Eme enjoys playing with poetic forms and the themes of identity, exploitation and the environment; he loves gardening and sometimes thinks himself a farmer. Tim hopes to revisit his long-abandoned prose manuscripts and treat them the way he treats his poetry manuscripts. He lives in Rivers; his work is published in *The Malahat Review*, *New Welsh Review*, *Magma*; *apt*, *The Fiddlehead* and *FIYAH*, etc. Tim studied engineering at the Niger Delta University, and is presently pursuing a BA in English Studies at the University of Port Harcourt.

Somnambulist

E. G. Condé

For generations, the kanoa drifted in the dark.

Orocobix slumbered within, watching, waiting. The craft jostled as the gravitic maw of the nightsea gripped its calcite hull. Clutched by dark currents, it plunged, bound for a turquoise sphere that shimmered like an island in the oceanic void. The kanoa trembled as it bore thro□gh a fiery membrane of sky, amid spooling carmine clouds. As its bony shell withered in the infernal crucible, the living vessel screeched in agony.

Sharing its pain, Orocobix awakened. The little coral polyps that were the kanoa, the beings that served as caretakers for Orocobix's slumbering body, were dying. Their bony carapaces slo□ghed into the firmament as the craft pl□mmeted toward a marbled landscape of brown decay and green perseverance. Orocobix bid the polyps a grateful farewell before detaching their body from the corals' vitreous tethers. After centuries of sleep, Orocobix was ready to shed the comfort of the kanoa and walk among the undreaming.

Orocobix leapt into the sky, recalling previous lives, when they had been others who dived into azure waters from leafy mountain perches to spear wriggling fish or to catch a ricocheting, resin ball amid a batey court of sculpted monoliths. To slow their approach, Orocobix opened their feathered arms, harvesting the energy of the wind column. Below, a colossal wreck peered over an arid landscape. Amid tawny, xeric jags, a cylindrical machina jutted toward the heavens. Clumps of neon-pink moss sought to slow the advance of its synthetic corr□ption, b□t their efforts were f□tile. The pink flora was retreating as steel tentacles retic□lated o□t into the land, staining the soil gray with their deepening incursion.

Orocobix steered their body to line up with the lofty rim of the great cylinder, catching in their peripheral vision the last of the kanoa sputtering into a plume of gold-blue flame. They decelerated, scarlet tail plumes scattering as two pairs of fibrous wing-arms unspooled from their back. The appendages, a weft of living yuca roots tightly braided to soak up air, stabilized their descent to the machina below, but the air was foul with caustics from its foul industry. Their netted wings were swiftly dissolving in the corrosive currents. Orocobix elongated their body, lunging their taloned feet to catch the charred sill of the cylindrical engine just as their wings gave out. They perched atop the machina, peering down to the darkened bottom, where their quarry, a fell engine, hummed and pulsed in bright viridian bursts.

With their wings destroyed, Orocobix had to find another way down to the base of the wreck.

"Nasa," Orocobix commanded, their voice a guttural song, between bird and human.

From a cotton pouch woven on their reed sash, they tossed a dozen soapstones into the chasm below, watching the glinting missiles transmute into the slick, amber bodies of tiny tree frogs. The cokís sung as they leapt in tandem below, trailing a resinous skein in their wake. When they reached the bottom of the wreck, their pitched cries suddenly went silent as their bodies gave way to lithe cassava roots that spiraled up along the resin track to the rim of the engine where Orocobix waited patiently.

Just as Orocobix positioned themselves to rappel down the cassava latticework to the reactor below, their human ears discerned something approaching from the wreck. The metallic droning that permeated the wreck was unmistakable; the voracious ones, the island-eaters, had come.

Orocobix unsheathed a spicate macana from the coral scabbard fused to their back.

The Astrals encircled, a trio of floating, rust-iron husks, jagged proboscises oozing beneath smoldering glass eyes. Orocobix delved deep into the ancestral wisdom, recounting ancient battles with rival Caribs, plumbing the memories for tactics, but the Astrals moved too quickly. There was no time to consult the matriline for strategy. Orocobix struck first, their flowing scarlet tail-capes cascading in sinuous, feathery flourishes as the ribbed macana met decaying steel.

The first of the trio fell readily in a burst of white sparks and splintered metal. The second darted away, but Orocobix tracked it. They spun their body swiftly to pierce its beaming eye, making sure to shatter the glass that encased its simulacrum of sentience. Orocobix then turned to face their final foe, and the bobbing drone lunged its proboscis at Orocobix's sternum, between their breasts, nearly piercing their vulnerable human heart. Orocobix parried, but they over-extended, and the macana flew into the sky before tumbling down into the heart of the wreck.

Orocobix was unarmed.

The Astral approached, and Orocobix imagined that it hungered so greatly that it felt pain. But Orocobix knew better than to regard the Astrals as anything but mirages of the living, an amalgam of many lost tribes; the Siyno'USAh, the Ruso-EU, the undreaming machina they worshipped and even the Iber who sieged Orocobix's little island in the cerulean. They were island-eaters.

Orocobix struck again. With one arm they grabbed the slithering proboscis, and with the other, they pried at the seams of the Astral's spherical dome. Orocobix pulled with the strength of their ancestors, ripping the fell beast into many pieces, until its glass eye was freed.

It fell and cracked before going dim.

Orocobix glimpsed their reflection in the inert glass sphere. Atop their head rested a crescent-shaped carapace, the smiling face of Guayaba, ruler of the realm beyond death, hewn in red-clay. Living roots of yuca fell in gnarled braids below their waist as the hair of their human ancestors had in Jatibonicu. In the deep sockets of the ochre mask, Orocobix's eyes fumed in hues of burnished amber, their black pupils shaped like slivered moons. Whereas the caciques had faces that terminated in rounded jaws and brown lips, the gold beak of an Inrirí jutted from the chin of Orocobix. Their body gleamed in a riot of color as they surveyed the wreck for other foes. Sweat poured down their neck, where a crimson-gold uanine amulet rested between scaly breasts. Orocobix repositioned their living headdress, drawing what sustenance they could from the pallid sun that lurked behind the chemical-doused clouds.

Just as Orocobix could feel the plant part of themselves making food from the sun, an Astral impaled their abdomen, its wriggling proboscis boring through flesh and sinew.

Orocobix roared with pain, whirling around to crush the Astral with the cracked eye that it had mistakenly thought destroyed. Even as the creature burst into flame and went still, Orocobix knew that it was too late. The Astral had fulfilled its purpose, and Orocobix had little time to spare to complete their errand.

Orocobix could feel venom seeping into their blood. While they slept, the Astrals had spread across sky and sea and land, corroding all that they touched until nothing lived in the universe without knowing the shadow of their decay. Like the Yurakans of old, they raged and swelled in a mighty cyclone that grew as it consumed. Unlike the deity-storms, however, whose calamitous ire gave way to righteous flourishing, the Astrals brought no renewal to the archipelagoes of the nightsea that they decimated. Orocobix cawed in agony, not at the unbearable sensation of death creeping into their body, but at the prospect of failure. For Orocobix now bore the weight of a civilization. They were the whole of the island of Borikén made flesh. Failure meant extinction.

But they had survived extinction before. They could survive it again.

The cassava net, like the ancient nasa used to trap fish in shallow waters, held the weight of Orocobix with ease as they nimbly strafed from lattice to lattice down the chasm. Pain slowed their descent into the derelict abyss. The cavernous dark of the machina did not trouble Orocobix, the plankton fused with their skin emitting a cobalt phosphorescence that rendered much of the expanse below visible. Instead, they found themselves haunted by a double-presence in their thoughts, an alien Other attempting to take hold. Orocobix's limbs loosened, an enervation brought on by the toxin.

It was not long before Orocobix slipped, crashing in a burst of feathers and blood on the rusted jags at the bottom of the machinic wreck.

Orocobix drifted between planes, aware faintly of the hum of the reactor just meters away from their mangled body. A specter appeared. It took the shape of the first chief of the Iber to arrive on Borikén. The Colón, it called itself. Its pale skin was the hue of bone and its face was matted with black fur. It probed Orocobix's mind, desperate to learn how Orocobix had evaded the Astrals for all these centuries. It sifted through the ancestral rivers. It prodded their memories, attempting to excavate the lost history of how the beings they called Taíno were not extinct as their machina-shamans had said.

Orocobix did not bother to resist the invader, but gave it what it wanted: A memory from *then*, the before, on the island of Borikén; a painted chief on the lush slopes of Lukiyó immolating himself, burning to ash the accumulated heirlooms of his fore-mothers and their brothers, burning the birds, and the corals, and the fish, and the cassava, and all that lived on the island of Borikén. The onlookers, the first victims of the Ibers' blight, had collected up the ashes and stowed the remains of their leader in a calabash. They waited for the whirling Yurakan to come, beseeching it to carry the traces of Borikén into the turey beyond the sky. For many generations, the ashes drifted the nightsea, before metamorphosing into Orocobix, who then slept, waiting in the kanoa for the Iber who became Astrals to weaken.

And now Orocobix had awakened to sow Borikén anew in the sidereal archipelagos beyond the Ibers' wrecked Terra.

The Colón kept plumbing deeper into Orocobix, seeking the hidden knowledge of ancestors, but Orocobix denied the Colón. They drank a vial of the Mabí, their only defense against the blight that was assimilating them thought by tremulous thought.

Having momentarily silenced the Colón and numbed the pain of their broken limbs, Orocobix stood to full height. Before them, the reactor churned, its viridian beacon lancing into the clotted sky. With each pulse of its fell light, the unworlding engine sapped the island's vibrancy, assimilating all fugitive traces of life that resisted, snuffing out all the dreams of pink moss that sought to blanket their world in soft lush.

Orocobix limped forward, faintly aware of movement in their peripherals, even as blood oozed from their head. The Colón, now severed from their mind, had summoned the last of its Astrals to subdue Orocobix. The shambling figures, obscured in the dark, resembled the jellyfish that once bobbed in Yocahu's tides. Orocobix reached for an object stowed away in a satchel of leaves on its waist.

The Astrals encircled Orocobix, their pulsing eyes emitting light erratically as they unsheathed their glittering tentacles, preparing to strike and devour the last of the Borikén.

Orocobix opened a folded flamboyan leaf. Within slept a cemí, a crescent of ochre stone. Through their entanglement with the Astral consciousness, Orocobix learned that Iber had once excavated a number of cemí, regarding them as inert stones fashioned in the likeness of false deities. Their true purpose had eluded the Iber and their Astral successors.

Orocobix tossed the cemí hewn with the smiling face of Guayaba into the reactor just as the metallic arachnids began to impale their body.

The blight coursed through Orocobix as it had their ancestors on Borikén, erasing their memories, replacing their limbs with iron nodes, their living cells with silicon micro-processors—but none of it mattered. The reactor quaked, and from the cemí sprouted the many emerald shoots of a Cojóbana tree in a radial arc that pirouetted upward, engulfing and dismembering Orocobix and the spindly Astrals as it leapt up toward the sun. The Cojóbana sprouted, carrying the remains of Orocobix with it, interring them in a living cocoon of bough and leaf, where they flourished, between dreaming and wakefulness, a Somnambulist.

The Cojóbana that was also Orocobix dreamt of Borikén, sowing their memory-vision into the calamitous flesh of the planet at the edge of the nightsea until, at last, Borikén was remade.

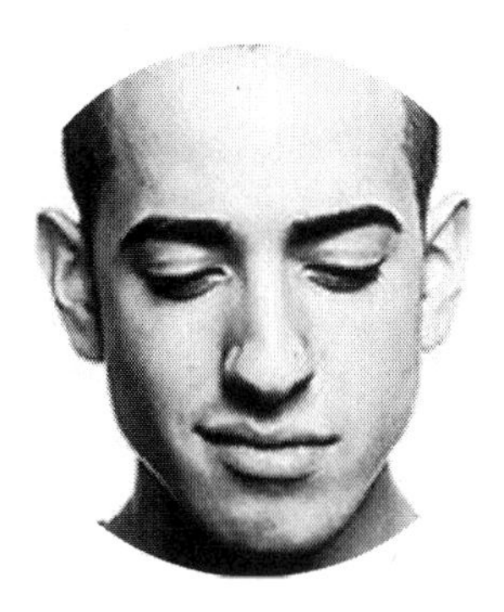

E.G. Condé (he/him) is an Anthropologist of technology and a queer boricua imagineer of speculative fiction, fantasy, and horror. His short fiction appears in *Anthropology & Humanism* and *If There's Anyone Left*. When he isn't conjuring up faraway universes or nearly possible futures, you might find him traversing the world in search of sand dunes to hike on.

The Loss of the Moon

Ken Poyner

I saw the moon come down.
I was driving that old stretch
Between home and late night,
Not another car on the road,
The moon the only real light
In a sky pitted with enough clouds
To chase off most stars. The moon
Made enough of a hole to lick
The dark itself. But then
The moon started to come down.
As if inch by inch, though
That seemed but an optical illusion
Given my angle and distance. I watched
It sliding lower, eyes darting back
To the ever-darkening road often enough
That I could drive without slowing,
My wife expecting me home on time.
Finally, it was out of sight, lost
In the trees. I did not actually see
It crash, nor did I feel
Earthquake or rumble, collision
Or fevered merge. The conclusion
Was simply the dark sky, the darker
Road, and I thought the tides,
The tides.

Ken’s fo□r collections of brief fictions and fo□r collections of poetry can be fo□nd at Amazon and most online booksellers. He spent 33 years in information system management, is married to a world record holding female power lifter, and has a family of several cats and betta fish. Individ□al works have appeared in *Café Irreal*, *Analog*, *Danse Macabre*, *The Cincinnati Review*, and several h□ndred other places. He has had seven P□shcart nominations witho□t fielding a single win. www.kpoyner.com.

Wildfire, Hellfire: the Case for Siberian Globeflowers

Sofia Ezdina

I.

My home was on fire.

Wildfires came with vengeance in late J□ly, eng□lfed the forest and t□rned it to cinders.

It is a place with a long memory: centenarian pines reached to the skies, mantled the mountain's spine like a rustling shroud, deep-green, dark-green, emerald-green. In winter, they covered themselves with sparkling white, thick and noble. It was a home: for foresters, for lynxes, for bears, for me, for globeflowers. The globeflowers: they glowed like gems, little lights in the malachite of lush greenery. In bloom, they turned into a sea, mirroring the scorching copper sun.

We call Siberian globeflowers *zharki*. "Little fires".

We say that taiga sings. The choir of the trees is not a hymn nor a dirge; it's a lullaby, and with it, a memory. This is where loneliness ends. For generations of exiles and vagabonds, nomads and runaways; for me. You can go to the past and gather this memory like seashells, fragment by fragment, if you simply walk south along the Yenisei river, past Sayan Mountains, past Venuses of Mal'ta, then circling back north. There yo□ will find their (o□r)—o□r (my)—my loneliness buried.

Now, all that is left are ashes, remnants of what once was beautiful.

According to the Aerial Forest Protection Service, on August 20, 2019, eighty-five forest fires ran amok in R□ssia, partic□larly in Siberia and the Far East.[1] The largest area ablaze was Krasnoyarsk Krai, my home region; there were fifty-three centers of ignition.

Three days earlier the number was one hundred and twelve. A month before, it was one hundred and twenty-six.

At the end of J□ly, the fires were still largely ignored, beca□se, as the authorities put it, "There is no threat to settlements and objects of the economy, and the predicted cost of extinguishing fires exceeds the predicted damage caused by them", even though the combusting area was approaching three million hectares.

A significant part of the burning land was in so-called 'control zones'—remote areas deemed uninhabited. In 2015, a law was passed establishing the right of regional authorities to determine firefighting in these territories economically inexpedient. This formally legalized the practice that historically developed from regional poverty—there was no money, no fuel, no planes to land firefighters in remote territories. In Soviet times, many fires were not extinguished—there was no satellite monitoring, and no one counted them.

The regional officials refused to extinguish fires, but they were not the only ones to blame. Federal funding for forest protection is calculated based on the acreage of areas marked for conservation, excluding control zones. Expected costs in control zones, in the logic of the authorities, are always higher than the damage done. Damage is measured at the minimum value of the wood, if it were to be cut and processed for lumber (and if that process is considered economically infeasible, there is no damage). The region must either spend its own funds to put out fires in control zones or do nothing.

My home was on fire, and they said fire cost nothing.

So the governors are officially entitled to refuse to extinguish wildfires if it's not economically profitable. The head of the Federal Forestry Agency explained it this way: "See for yourself: the closest tanker plane's base point is 500 kilometers from the fire in the taiga. It flies back and forth, dumps a small amount of water. We'll go bankrupt using aviation for such purposes". The Krasnoyarsk Krai governor said: It's a common natural phenomenon which is pointless, and perhaps even harmful, to fight. "If we have a snowstorm in winter, it doesn't occur to anyone to melt the icebergs to make the weather warmer."

I watch the forest burn—full of horror and rage, and something sharper and more terrible: loss.

My home was on fire, and they said it was economically unprofitable to save it.

Siberian Wildfires
Daria Kholyavka

II.

The truth is: the control zones are not as deserted as they're trying to assure us— there are settlements on their borders, roads and developed logging forests. Wildfires roared in a twenty-kilometer radius near the nine settlements in Evenkia. The closest fire to the village of Kuyumba burned five kilometers away; ashes fell on the courtyards, breathing was a struggle, and at two or three hundred meters nothing was visible.

It is impossible to estimate how many animals have died in the fire. Residents of the northern territories saw animals on the roads, driven away from the taiga, more and more. They came to settlements. For several days, a bear lived in one of the villages after running away from the burning boondocks.

The flaming sea of globeflowers, "little fires", now was a hellfire circle.

Smoke overtook several neighboring territories at once. Unlike the usual sequence, when smoke goes north, that year it turned west, to the more populated parts of the country. Sunday morning, July 21, when Novosibirsk was overtaken by smog, the radio broadcasted: nothing to worry about; it is not smoke, but mist.

People were suffocating, and the first motion was to say that everything was fine.

NASA published a photo showing a smoke plume spreading over the Krasnoyarsk Krai. A significant part of Siberia and the Ural cities were under a dense, cindered veil.

The extent to which forest fires affect human health is still poorly understood, with the exception that products of combustion can settle in the lungs and contribute to the development of asthma and allergies. The air in Novosibirsk was certainly damaging: the maximum permissible concentration of suspended particles per million was exceeded by 1.5 times.[2] People complained of the acrid taste of smog. There were noticeably fewer insects, since the aerosol curtain created by smoke blocked the functioning of the midge's nervous and respiratory systems.[3] The number of ambulance calls due to smoke increased by over 15%.[4] Cinders can lead to an increase in mortality from chronic respiratory diseases, an increase in mortality among the elderly, and an increase in miscarriages. But it's impossible to attach these deaths to a specific fire, and it's impossible to get any insurance or compensation.

People were suffocating and there was no one to blame.

III.

Why did fires occur?

Officially, the fires were explained by abnormal weather: high temperature in the absence of rains, dry thunderstorms, short snow cover in winter. They talked about thirty-degree heat and lightning strikes.

But Russian WWF, on the contrary, claimed that in 95% of cases, forest fires are anthropogenic.[5] From natural causes—lightning or abnormal heat—conflagrations rarely appear.

Most of the fires are man-made; they occurred mainly as a result of forest felling, because of the burning of logging residues. Often, people deliberately light fires to get rid of old, dry grass. Bonfires and cigarette butts can also contribute. It's a small contribution, but a contribution nonetheless; one more *zharok* on the funeral pyre.

These small fires could definitely have been put out right away, but the local authorities refused to, leading to the large outbreaks, which turned into an unsolvable problem: all we could do was wait for the rain. The situation got out of control precisely because it was decided not to extinguish the fires while they were small. Officials tried to attribute everything to nature, because it was convenient to look for an excuse in the elements, in processes that we cannot control.

My home was on fire, and it was impossible to save it.

IV.

What for the future?

According to Greenpeace, by the beginning of August 2019, fires in Siberia reached record levels in the entire history of observation, since 2001: in acreage of burning area, burnt woodland, and the amount of carbon dioxide emitted into the atmosphere.[6] Each year, on average, three times more forest dies in fires than the forestry industry processes. Forest resources are already scarce—because of fires and beca⊡se of logging—and it will only grow worse.

The ⊡n⊡s⊡ally powerf⊡l and rapid spread of fires is connected to the environmental situation. Climate change leads to more extreme weather events: somewhere it rains for a long time, somewhere, on the contrary, severe dro⊡ghts occ⊡r, leading to wildfires. In Russia, the Irkutsk region faced both in 2019: at the beginning of s⊡mmer, the flood, then—savage forest fires.

Wildfires happen in nat⊡re. Each ecosystem has its dist⊡rbance regime. For pinewood, fires occ⊡r once every 50-100 years as part of normal forest dynamics. Some areas burn out, and new ecological communities hatch upon them, while protected areas remain in good condition. The pine has thick bark, and it's q⊡ite resistant to fires. In b⊡rned areas, windthrows wrest o⊡t dead roots, exposing new soil—and plants that cannot germinate in dense underlay sprout here. On this mineralized surface, they can thrive. This process contributes to the normal functioning of large ecological systems.

When industrialized humans intervene in this system, instead of igniting once every 100 years, the forest combusts once every two or three years, and in some places even more often. And the climate imbalance means minimal foci of ignition lead to much greater conseq⊡ences. A technogenic wildfire is not a fire that renews the ecosystem—but one that degrades and in places even eliminates it. *Zharki* will grow here no longer.

Climate change is merciless, and it prisons us all.

V.

It's been more than a year since wildfires came. Many forests over the world experienced the same loss and sorrow and ire.

The fire came with a vengeance, not j⊡st for wood, b⊡t for ⊡s, with grief and resentment, so sharp and full of contempt.

The fires come from tradition, ignorance, ins⊡fficient funding, thoughtless legislation. From illegal logging, littering, a carefree attitude to nature. From poor communication. And most of all: from an unwillingness to see the problem as a problem until it knocks on the door with l⊡rid fists.

The fire comes from corporations that t⊡rn the atmosphere into a greenho⊡se. They c⊡t down trees, strip off their bark, flay, manufacture, grind, kiln, soak, compress, make paper and write on it about the terrible state of the forests.

The fires come from □s. Beca□se we b□rn logging resid□es, beca□se we leave bonfires, beca□se we throw cigarette b□tts, and because we refuse to extinguish what can be extinguished. All this—in conditions of heat, of dro□ght and strong wind —grows more extreme and more dangerous.

The fire comes from officials, from the government; from the comforting tho□ght that fighting nat□ral phenomena is pointless (and perhaps even harmful). From our failure to consider nature as a f□ndamentally essential reso□rce, rather than as something that can be priced and sold.

Taiga, somehow, forgave us so much. It forgave us Gulags, and katorga, and Decembrists, and hidden bones, and taking and taking and taking and never taking enough. I wonder if it forgives being neglected.

We say that taiga sings. The choir of the trees is not a hymn nor a dirge; it's a lullaby, and with it, a memory.

Now my home is on fire; we cannot redeem it.

Notes

1. https://aviales.ru/popup.aspx?news=5549
(English machine translation)
2. https://www.kommersant.ru/doc/4032981
(English machine translation)
3. https://ngs.ru/text/summer/2019/07/26/66174625/
(English machine translation)
4. https://ecfor.ru/publication/lesnoj-pozhar-sibir-ekonomika/
(English machine translation)
5. https://www.kommersant.ru/doc/4046333#id1776662
(English machine translation)
6. https://greenpeace.ru/blogs/2019/08/05/lesnye-pozhary-v-sibiri-je-to-klimaticheskij-krizis/ (English machine translation)

Sofia Ezdina is a writer and q□eer woman from R□ssia, who befriends stray animals and whispers eerie things. Her works have appeared in *Jalada Africa*, *Enchanted Conversation*, and *Funicular Magazine*. One of her poems was also named as a runner-up for Barjeel Poetry Prize. You can stalk her on Twitter, which remains inconveniently bilingual.

Daria Kholyavka is a beginner 2D artist from St. Petersburg keen on nature and its habitants. Nevertheless, she wants to be strong like a woman who fights bears in a forest. This piece is dedicated to the Siberian wildfires of 2019 in her home region and aims to enco□rage more people to take care of o□r planet. Yo□ can find more of her artwork on her Behance.

Dramatis Personae of the Apocalypse

Avra Margariti

i. The Artist

Agrees blood doesn't make for the best paint,
but humans will use worse through history,
whelk dye and highly toxic cinnabar,
the mollusks mourning their mass murder,
the painters' lungs shriveled with poison for eternity.
The artist immortalizes sunsets and war-zones.
They name each stone canvas imperial purple,
vermilion, carmine, crimson,
but the truth is, they're just red.
Everyone is red.

ii. The Poet

Roams battlefields in search of personal effects
harvested from those dead or dying,
for tragedy births the best poems.
Dog tags, torn or scorched photographs,
hand-carved bone figurines of a serene woman
who might have been peace, personified.
The poet takes his razor-edged pen
and scratches palimpsests of history
across his heaving chest.

iii. The Scientist

Tries to detect water in the dacryphiliac desert.
She dowses through endless expanses of cracked earth,
holding on to the forked wishbone
of some long-extinct animal, carving spirals in the sand.
Her feet blister and her skin melts off in rivulets

before her fossilized rod palpitates.
An absinthe-green lake, a promised oasis.
The desert floor opens wide to swallow her,
the trilobites and arthropods welcoming her home.

iv. The Teacher

Fails to convince his students of his prophetic visions.
Long before the first local conspiracy theory
or worldwide panicked broadcast,
he drew chalk figures across the blackboard,
interpretations of death and destruction
like geoglyphs or paleolithic cave art.
The teacher begged his students and their families
to gather provisions and build underground bunkers,
to save themselves any way they could.
But even then, he was too late.
Their creator had already sealed their fate,
painted in red pigment across the walls.

Avra Margariti is a queer author, Greek sea monster, and Pushcart-nominated poet with a fondness for the dark and the darling. Avra's work haunts publications such as *Vastarien*, *Asimov's*, *Liminality*, *Arsenika*, *The Future Fire*, *Space and Time*, *Eye to the Telescope*, and *Glittership*. "The Saint of Witches", Avra's debut collection of horror poetry, is forthcoming from Weasel Press. Yo⊡ can find Avra on twitter (@avramargariti).

Onions

Grace Wagner

"Men argue. Nature acts."

—Voltaire

Palm trees wave their heavy heads,
canna lilies rise brilliant and bloody
in their beds, and the tide floods the streets.
They call it s□nny day flooding, beca□se it hasn't rained
for weeks, and still the water comes.
I haven't cried in weeks, and still—

I hear the polar caps are nearly free
of ice, that the sea will rise and don't I know it?
My car fo□nders in the flood.
I like to think this is the only thing stopping me
from finding yo□,

but that isn't true.
The tide swept in and took you away. At least

that is what I say when people ask where you are.
I know it sounds like you're dead, forgive me
if I find that easier.
I've tried to live consciously, nothing
without purpose, to do nothing
without consideration for the world
I inhabit.

Since you left, I've kept
all the lights on. Since you left,
I drive my car endlessly around the neighborhood.
I eat beef and candy, and I'm thinking
of having a pool put into the backyard, thinking
abo□t b□ying an SUV.

Onions

The water burbles up through storm drains, seeps
into the roots of our garden, kills
our onions with salt. Which is okay, I guess,
since you planted them.

The Po'ouli

Grace Wagner

(listed as extinct in 2018)

Little black-headed song
bird, discovered
only recently—1973,
  the year Secretariat won
  the Triple Crown—so much
  relentless muscle

racing a circle
while this cryptic bird
flitted ⊡p Haleakala's
  steep slope—moss-tangled,
  dripping ferns—snapping up
  snails and waxworms.

Now imagine this:
a last ditch effort,
venturing across
  the volcanic crater
  with padded boxes,
  hoping to catch

the last three
specimens—perhaps
a breeding pair—
  256 birds captured, but no
  Po'o⊡li—fifteen years
  later they would declare

the bird extinct—another
in a long line lost
to invasive species,

disease,
and habitat destruction.
The people who tried

to save this little bird
are immune
to despair—
they suspend
themselves
from ropes,

pollinate flowers
when the pollinators
have died—
they trek
the rainforest
playing calls

from long dead birds,
but you, little bandit,
refuse the call—
there is no hope
but we can't help
ourselves,

we believe in miracles—
a songbird waiting
to be discovered.

Grace Wagner is a queer, nonbinary, neurodivergent poet and artist living with a disability in Denver, Colorado. They hold an MFA in Poetry and a certificate in Women, Gender, and Sexuality Studies from the University of Houston where they studied with Martha Serpas, Kevin Prufer, and Erin Bellieu. They have previously studied with Carolyn Forché, Robert Pinsky, and others. They were awarded an Academy of American Poets Prize in 2020, and their work can be found in *Salmagundi Magazine*, *The Atlanta Review*, *Hayden's Ferry Review*, *The Offing*, *The Adroit Journal*, and elsewhere. For more, visit www.gracewagnerpoet.com.

When Teens Turned Into Trees

Sigrid Marianne Gayangos

So j□st when h□mans started dying d□e to mass s□ffocation for lack of air to breathe, the teens took it upon themselves to solve the problem and took root—literally. The adults weren't so s□rprised, as one wo□ld imagine, when the first girl t□rned into a st□rdy Narra tree with dainty yellow flowers. Wasn't that what rebellious teenagers do anyway? It was just a phase, they said; soon she'd shake off that dark brown bark and carry on with life. When another teen, a boy this time, turned into a Banaba tree with delicate p□rple-pink flowers, they believed it was more or less the same thing.

It started with the teens stubbornly standing their ground, until their feet grew roots spreading earthwards, until their slender torsos expanded in diameter, until their hands became branchless stems extending skywards, until they started eating the sun, until the wind gushed shadowy and restless among them. When they refused to return to their human forms in time for dinner, their mothers pleaded and cried in front of them. But didn't mothers often cry for their children anyway? So it was the same, I suppose. The teenage trees remained quiet, and yet their silence was alive, palpable even.

My mother feared for my sister, who had then just turned fifteen. When she stood on the same spot o□tside for min□tes on end, Mama would go hysterical and shove her back into the house. She would then obsessively scan my sister from head to toe, looking for telltale signs of transformation: hair that resembled a lush canopy, stretch marks that started to feel like deep furrows on a trunk, a hangnail so jagged and torn it looked like lateral roots. There were none, and Mama would give a sigh of relief.

The thing with teenagers turning into trees, though, was that there seemed to be no discernible pattern. First it was that girl who never missed Sunday church services, then the middle boy of the seven Santos children, then four seniors secretly smoking a joint behind the dumpster, then an entire group of youth volunteers.

Some boys grew into fruit-bearing trees, some girls never bore fruits. All turned into providers of shade and drinkers of rain water. No one knew if the change had anything to do with genetics. The change came sudden, too. Maybe it was a wordless breath of wood, inhaled and nurtured within the body until it was ready to merge with the soil; maybe the seed had been there all along.

A Facebook Live post—that was how we learned my sister had turned. Our phones buzzed with the incessant vibration from consecutive notifications. We saw it, Isabel planting her feet firmly on the ground, her hands reaching out to the sky, a serene smile on her face. Then her human body was enveloped into the darkest of trunks, her arms lengthened until stunning fire-red blooms shaped like sea anemones appeared on her hands. My sister had turned into a Mangkono tree, and, in a way, it made sense to me. Her love for the color red manifested in the flowers she carried. Her sheer stubbornness, in the hard wood that required a sturdy diamond-point saw just to slice through it. And, of course, she chose to plant herself just outside the city library.

My mother had never missed a day dropping by the library since then. Often, she brought my sister's favorite treats with her, as if these might somehow make her change back and enjoy all humanly pleasures. All across the city, it was not uncommon to see people talking yearningly to trees, while some even took to sleeping in tents just to be beside their trees. As months passed, the trees grew in number and in strength. We watched as birds started flying in to nest, we watched as what had formerly been an asphalt furnace turned into a lovely tree-lined street. And the air... it was just so, so much easier to breathe.

The teens continued to change and I knew that soon it would be my time. My friends and I, we skipped school. What was the point of school anyway, if our future meant simply standing still and dancing to the wind with our leafy branches? Instead, we read about photosynthesis, pollination and meristematic cells. We figured things would become second nature once we turned, but there was no harm in having theoretical knowledge as well.

The teens had not matured into adults, so a number of universities had to shut down, and the younger children were allowed to run wild. Several families had moved out of the neighborhood, thinking that the epidemic was contained in our tiny portion of the world, only to find out later on that it was all the same, except their children turned into foreign trees like pines and willows.

A year had passed and I watched as our bustling city turned into some sort of a ghost town. Not so long ago, the parched earth was slowly puckering into shingles. Now, trees of different types towered around us, their roots sinking deep into the now fertile soil. Every day, we looked up and saw the leaves forming an umbrella over us and said a prayer of thanks. Every day, I looked up and wondered if enough teens had turned for us to have another shot at surviving.

The trees stood stubborn and tall, giving us air and shade, and saved us from this drowning world. I had always wanted to become a doctor, but I had never said it out loud. Instead, I kept this hopeful wish to myself and only whispered it to the gibbous moon. A breeze stirred in our quiet neighborhood—the silence only broken by the birds nestled in the branches above me, saying good night to one another at the same time. I stood perfectly still and allowed the night's calm to embrace me.

Then I tried lifting my leg to head back home, but I found myself unable to move. I sighed. Perhaps I could still save humanity this way. Perhaps, one day, we would all be saved. But, for now, I could only watch as white cottony blossoms of a Salimbobong tree began to surround me, as if falling from my own head.

Sigrid Marianne Gayangos was born and raised in Zamboanga City, Philippines. Her works have appeared in various venues such as *Cha: An Asian Literary Journal*, *OMBAK Southeast Asia's Weird Fiction Journal*, *ANMLY*, *Likhaan: The Journal of Contemporary Philippine Literature*, and *Everything Change: An Anthology of Climate Fiction*, among others. Her debut short story collection, *Laut*, is forthcoming from the University of the Philippines Press.

E.I.

Kola Heyward-Rotimi

605,421,005 modular sensors floated across Earth's waters, analyzing around 54% of the oceans' chemical makeup. 26,304 of these sensors lay along the passenger ship Afẹmọj⊡*'s trans-Atlantic route. This was a microscopic percentage of the global sensor count, but sufficient to keep track of the vessel's trail of pollutants. The crew and passengers were aware that their voyage would be gaining a lot of attention from the planet, as* Afẹmọj⊡ *should have been decommissioned years ago. As monsoon season was reaching its peak along the eastern coast of Central and North America, most Atlantic transportation resources were in use up there, leaving behind sub-par equipment like this leaky vessel that ran partially on bunker fuel. Despite* Afẹmọj⊡*'s many renovations over the decades, she couldn't help dumping sulfur oxide into the atmosphere that eventually seeped into the planet's water supply.*

Each sensor bobbing on the waves tasted the air and water that Afẹmọj⊡ *left tainted in her wake and spoke to their neighbor. After the ship had traveled a little over 1,000 kilometers, the cumulative amount of pollution produced had outweighed the acceptable ratio for a vessel of her size. 5,203 sensors collectively filed a complaint against* Afẹmọj⊡*. It was placed in line behind hundreds more to be processed before it (ocean-related incidents only), and in twenty minutes the complaint was addressed by Earth. The ocean was given the go ahead by the planet.*

The Afẹmọj⊡ *captain's dashboard turned a deep blue as the engine was disabled by the sea. He'd half expected a shutdown to happen at some point on the way to Rio de Janeiro, but it was frustrating nonetheless. The captain, his crew, and their thousands of passengers would now wait for either the call to return home or for a drone fleet to provide assistance purifying their fuel. Without the engines, inertia pushed the vessel slightly off track. In the process, the ship's hull crushed a small, floating computer server coded by a child from Ibadan—a server they had built for a school project with their classmates. Next morning when the child woke up to find their virtual environment offline, they cried to their mother, who traced a couple report logs and discovered how the server was destroyed. Instead of explaining the chain of events that had led to her child's bad day, she thought it would be more interesting to blame it on Olóòkun, the god of all large waters, all oceans. In a sense, she was correct.*

While Afẹmọj⊡ *had landed the final blow, it had been on the sea's command.*

Prisca Brethers, the current Appalachia LF-4 Soil delegate, had arrived at the dig site. Her aide, Asmara, waded through the marsh in knee-high boots. Prisca preferred to lean against their ATV. They were at the f⊡rthest reaches of Prisca's j⊡risdiction, a flat stretch of swamp water and tangled, tropical vegetation. Braving the marsh was a battle that the humidity was winning, forcing Prisca to loosen the collar of her suit.

Asmara looked down at the water choked with algae.

"As they said, the b⊡ilding looks intact. Well . . . intact eno⊡gh. It should be easy to spin, Prisca."

"I'll take your word for it," Prisca said. She would check the subterranean layout of the swamp herself if not for the information streaming thro⊡gh her eyes' internal HUD. It was only possible to do so many things at once. The good thing was that the numbers were looking solid. Notifications for Prisca's speech had spread across Landfall Province 4, and a couple thousand locals were going to tune in.

It had been a year since she'd been elected delegate for her region, and the jitters that came before a speech still hadn't abated. The first day on the job had been the worst. Prisca had woken ⊡p to the call of Appalachia's soil union, congratulating her before explaining what she'd even done. Then came the formal invitation to serve her community for a two-year term.

While she'd undergone an abrupt, temporary change to her job description by being elected to the soil union, Prisca continued playing to her strengths. She had been a teacher, so that was how she hoped to encourage action in her community. A minute before the start of her broadcast she remembered the golden rule: speak to the children. Adults were also capable of learning, but they would be much more open to it if the youngest were on board.

Asmara came back to the ATV with two thumbs up. "We all good?"

"Yessir. Let's go."

With a smile, he moved to her side, brushing away the beads of sweat crawling down his forehead. There was no stretch of Earth directly untouched by human and robotic alterations except for a couple deep sea trenches, and this swamp was no exception, but the changes to the environment here were all about analyzing, not modifying. The heat was unadulterated—which would be a problem in the future if Prisca were successful today. One thing at a time.

Turning this stretch of swamp into a communal space for the region wo□ld be a herc□lean task in the first place, and Prisca wo□ld have to convince everyone that it was a good idea before worrying about the weather.

The schoolchildren and their teachers appeared before Prisca, their digital facsimiles overlaid across the swamp, streaming through her internal visual feed. She waved and the kids eagerly returned it, though that was pretty much it in terms of contact. She couldn't set up tactile feedback for this livestream, since it would've been too resource intensive after they'd already got permission to use the ATV. Hopefully this would teach the kids good social distancing practices, since the next plague had come to the region.

Asmara introduced Prisca as she eyed the viewer count ticking away in the corner of her eye. It was in the quadruple digits already. Each person tuning in was represented as a blinking green dot hovering above the sky like a new star field. Most of them were probably using this broadcast as background noise while making lunch or something, but still. Any of these people might get interested and swing the vote in her favor.

One dot came late. It was a dark blue, and it maintained a steady light. As it did with most political maneuvers, the planet would watch from a front row seat.

Asmara motioned Prisca forward.

"Hey y'all!" she said to the class, getting a chorus of greetings in response. Tho□gh this wo□ld co□nt as a field trip, these children didn't sound like they were interested. No point in boring them with the speech she'd practiced with Asmara beforehand. It was best to get to the f□n st□ff as fast as possible.

Prisca gave them the briefest history she could muster—a history of the ground, what laid under it, and who used to walk on it. The children all knew they lived in Eno and Occaneechi territory, but their historical knowledge of the USA's violent occupation would be murky at best. Just mentioning that fallen regime was enough to perk their interest. Some of their eyes lit up full of morbid curiosity, and others had small frowns on their faces.

"There's a relic from the time of the American Empire under our feet," Prisca said with the hyperbolic gravitas of a ghost story. "A really important, old building. As our community's soil delegate, one of my jobs is to find old buildings like this that were swallowed during the planet's big changes, and then I figure out what to do with them. For this one, I want us to work together and bring it back."

The children's blank stares agitated the butterflies in Prisca's stomach. Funny how her audience was immaterial, yet the nerves were just the same as if she were on a stage. Instead of falling into the queasiness of her anxiety, Prisca focused on what she could do to convince the kids and bystanders that their past was worth an appraisal.

It wasn't an easy task. A side-effect of the planet's transition into the Anthropocene, with all of the collapse and death that had entailed, was inherent distrust of the people and countries who came before. These children, as did their parents and grandparents, lived in spite of their ancestors' best attempts at eliminating their world. There was no love for the generations that had cashed in on transforming the Earth into a place unfit for the species that lived alongside the planet.

This was one of her more conservative political opinions, but Prisca didn't feel that hatred was the best answer to their past. At least, not as an all-encompassing response. She had no qualms with disavowing the ones who benefited off the ecological terror, as not only had they ruined the world for billions of people, they had also died before they could ever face the full, planetary consequences. Nothing good would come out of advocating for capitalists. But not everyone on Earth had been an orchestrator of this genocide.

"Under our feet is a big part of my people's history," Prisca said. "Hundreds of years ago they built a neighborhood where we stand right now, and hundreds of years before that they'd been in chains. They were forced into one of the worst situations of all time and they came out of it still creating. It's a bit of a miracle."

She told them about the neighborhood that had once stood

here when the land hadn't been swamp, about the legacy of this neighborhood, an oasis within the American regime's antiblack system. The b⊡ilding, M⊡t⊡al Tower, was one of the financial cornerstones that made this community possible. Prisca emphasized the concept of ref⊡ge fo⊡nd here, hoping the children wo⊡ld find a connection to their lives. As the planetary environment changed, all communities became places of respite.

Before the view count could start dipping, Prisca unveiled the 3D model of the structure submerged beneath them, rendered to scale across the marsh: a concrete highrise, built with the brashness of a civilization that tho⊡ght of str⊡ct⊡re and land as two different things. She let the kids loose. They ran about the building, spray cans materializing in their hands—one of the many skeuomorphic VR tools that had outlived the relevancy of their physical counterparts.

Then the history lesson was over, and the children came to say goodbye. The class dissolved into the air along with the viewers. All the green lights winked out, leaving the blue one on its own. It always took the planet a little longer to disengage from a broadcast since multiple sensory networks had to collate the terabytes of data they had collected over the course of the livestream.

"I'm feeling good about the vote," Asmara said. "You've been one of o⊡r most reso⊡rce-efficient delegates in a while, and this is yo⊡r first big project. My prediction is yo⊡'ll swing the majority."

Even though she felt the same, Prisca didn't want to jinx it by saying that out loud. She nodded along, looking at the water that came up to their shins, and imagined the building hidden beneath them. The stories it might have kept close.

50 kilometers northwest of Guiyang was a factory complex staffed by 6,230 adaptive computer numerical control machines, assigned to provide auxiliary construction resources for Khentii Seismic Province 2. Unlike their predecessors from around two hundred years ago, the machines employed an ecosystem of intracommunal sensor networks and smaller robots to adjust and readjust their manufacturing parameters, resulting in a factory that could run unattended by humans 95% of the time. This didn't make that remaining 5% any less critical.

During some downtime between active shifts, Building 3-A of the complex reported unapproved activity along its external wall. Unfortunately, this activity occurred in one of the four sensory blindspots in the two square kilometers of this factory complex, and there were no drones that could be diverted to deal with the situation. Most robotic labor was engaged with relocating crops after a major flood north of Shanghai. This led to a unanimous vote by the factory's workflow algorithms to call on human help. In came Wang Zhenxian, the closest person from the nearby hills, and a farmer in his free time. The factory debriefed him on their problem and reassured him that there should be no danger to his person. They only wanted him to get a good look, and the factory would tap into his visual feed so they might gain new perspective through his eyes.

Happy to do them this big favor, Wang made his way to the factory and saw it up close for the first time. Wang walked through the factory's near-empty streets, guided by his internal navi system to Building 3-A. There wasn't a window or door in sight. When he reached his destination, Wang caught himself and stayed back a little, not wanting to scare the trespassers off. He zoomed in and stabilized his vision so that the factory could watch as well. Perched on a ledge was a small family of sparrows. They had been pecking at the building's vents, attempting to build a nest in the ambient warmth, and they were probably the last of their species in this region. They had triggered the trespassing alert. Wang talked it over with the factory, and then he went home. At 3:00 AM that night, the factory complex was conscripted by Khentii S-2 for an emergency batch of 3D printer stepper motors. The adaptive CNC machines of Building 3-A remembered the sparrow nest and kept the noise under 45 dB so as not to scare them off. The sparrow nest covered a logo embossed on the vent, an ancient stamp that might have marked this factory as once the property of Foxconn, or Alibaba, or perhaps a different company entirely. A human had not stepped inside any of the buildings for over sixty years.

Throughout March, Prisca kept returning to that swamp. Every subsequent visit was through the remote services of an aerial drone, or a more terrestrial robot if she wanted some direct engagement with the wetlands and its underlying soil. It was for work, covering her bases in case there was an environmental violation or resource overreach, but Prisca had come to appreciate digging through the earth. A year ago she had barely recognized how to properly read pH, and now she pored over reams of technical reporting on her days off. To sift among the layers of peat, the new crops of vegetation that grew from it, along with the insects that had not only faced climate change but thrived in it—these gave her an unexpected connection to the environment she had been born and raised in. She had never disrespected it of course, but she'd assumed that it wasn't for her. Becoming her community's soil delegate was chipping away at her city girl tendency to deprioritize the natural landscape.

There was only so much double-checking one could do in a month. While her approval rating in the province was crawling upward, Prisca knew that the real voting bloc she had to impress was the planet. If the land didn't approve her historical restoration plan, she would be pushed back to square one. While gliding over the marsh canopy on a drone's camera feed, she could imagine Earth with a smug look and crossed arms, staring over her shoulder. Yes, it wasn't best practice to anthropomorphize the planet since humans were not the universal template for agency or intelligence. But it was more emotionally resonant to reduce the actions of the human species' geological progenitor, distill the planetary processes channeled through networked machines and simplify this world into something easy to confront. Something that didn't take all of humanity's brainpower to devise systems that made it communicable.

But again, there was only so much Prisca could do. On election night, she sat on the couch and scrolled through the chemical survey results that she'd collected over the past few weeks. Just to make sure. She splayed on the couch in her living room, reading the logs while chopping sounds echoed from the kitchen.

"Hey," Prisca's roommate Gwen shouted, taking a pause from whatever meal prep she was doing. "Asmara's at the door! I'll let him in yeah?"

Prisca looked up and gave the room a cursory glance for presentability. Mess-wise, things could have been much worse. Having windows open and catching the last moments of sunlight helped. The heat hadn't gone above 40 Celsius today, so it had been safe to circulate the outside air instead of relying on the apartment building's centralized AC.

Asmara strolled in with a smile and a bottle of champagne. Before Prisca could protest, he waved her back down on the couch and placed the bottle on her coffee table—not before wiping off the bottom with a handkerchief. While Asmara was a part of Prisca's hub of contacts who had tested negative for this decade's super virus, it was good etiquette to practice caution.

"Uh-uh," Asmara said, "I don't wanna hear it. We're celebrating your first restoration project no matter what way it goes."

She laughed in defeat, picking up the bottle. "How did you even get this?"

"One of the growers my side of town straight up gave it to me. I told him it was a special night and he's known me for a while, so he wanted to get me a gift."

With how dead the fields had been, it was a hell of a gift. Prisca's roommate came with some glasses and a tray of sliced mango. They didn't talk much, and food was their main avenue of interaction. Beyond that, Gwen wished her luck and retreated to her room. She'd be talking to her husband who was up the coast repairing New York's sea walls, so Prisca warned Asmara they should try and keep it down.

They put the poll numbers up and watched them tick against the window. Prisca found it surprisingly natural to be both nervous and bored. A couple drinks in, she talked with Asmara about their chances, and what might swing the vote one way or the other. He thought talking to the children was the best strategy Prisca could've gone with. Their excitement playing about the virtual rendition of the restored building was all the endorsement the community needed. The past couple of years had grown increasingly austere, and it looked like the future wouldn't improve on things. Not with the diminishing crop returns, and the heat that would soon force them to follow the paths of their Piedmont province neighbors down south, retreating into closed ecological systems. They needed a win now more than ever.

It seemed like they would get it. By the time the stars were coming out and the moon was staring down Prisca's street, 90% of the votes had been processed and more than 70% were in her favor. Then it would be Earth's turn. She'd bothered Asmara with the likelihood of harebrained scenarios and turns of events for so long that he had to get Prisca to stand down.

The province was done, and for her first proposed project, the response was solid. If they could only pause it here, clink glasses, and get to work, Prisca would've been ecstatic. But of course, after the complete statistics flashed on screen for a minute or two, the green bars and percentages melted away to be replaced by the planet's favorite shade of blue. It was a pulsing color, like it had a breath all its own—and it had taken hers away.

Two words faded in. *Revision Needed.* Then it was over.

Asmara raised his glass in excitement, spilling a few precious drops of champagne on the table surface. Prisca sat, deflated, and waved at the display still printed along her windowpane.

"Can you not read or something?"

"Seems like I can read better than you, Prisca! Congratulations."

"Congratulations on what?" She already waved away the verdict, delving into the data behind it. An extensive list of calculations filled the air before them. It wasn't the most practical way to process this data but she didn't feel like standing up and fetching a proper screen. After the loss, she wasn't planning on getting up from the couch for a while.

She wasn't in the headspace to give this the attention it needed, but the gist was obvious. The cumulative data collection from the marsh's monitoring systems had compared the power needed to restore the building compared to what was available in the area, to the effect on the local ecosystem, to what those resources might instead be used for.... If the planet had shared the entirety of its thought process with Prisca and Asmara on this single issue alone, they would have been left processing it for the rest of their lives. The worst part with the decentralized intelligence of a planet was how it could never point you to a single reason for failure. Instead, there was an endless list.

"Hey," Asmara said, grabbing Prisca's hand and whisking her from the streams of data. "I know that you're new to this position—which is the whole point of why it exists—but you gotta understand, this is excellent. For your first project at that? Doesn't matter if you're a soil or atmo or a damn water delegate, the first idea you float into the scene tends to get shot down immediately. This isn't even a dismissal!"

"I know. It's a revision. But on what?"

"That's for ⊡s to fig⊡re o⊡t, I g⊡ess," he said with a sip of champagne. "That's why I got us drinking before the verdict. It takes the edge off the work ahead."

She refilled her glass. Maybe he was onto something with that. There was not a chance Prisca would get over the Earth's dismissal by tonight, or possibly not by this week, but she didn't want to stop here. Not while her province responded so positively to the project.

Living mainly among humans, it was easy to forget that they weren't the only ones who held a stake in the land. When Prisca was reminded of the others involved, it sometimes felt like an imbalance when it was actually sharing. On the next draft, she'd listen a little harder to what the swamps said.

Virtually all drones employed by the planetary sensor grid ran on legacy software. Good software, but legacy, because humans had taken recycling to heart and it would take catastrophic failure before any firmware was rewritten. 1,000 kilometers west of South America, in Carnegie Ridge Province 12, the Galápagos Islands were a natural memorial to the extinction of over 500 endemic species that had once lived there. Due to risen sea levels and extreme heat, all wildlife were now skeletons wedged between shelves of cooled lava. Intermittent volcanic activity over the past few centuries kept the peaks of Isabela just above sea level. The island was barren, sloped expanses of pumice.

Five years ago, after decades of being devoid of life, Isabela welcomed its first visitors again. One of the mistakes that had been nestled within the drones' firmware had become amplified over hundreds of incremental updates. A single, bungled mathematical operation in the drones' navigation algorithm resulted in the coordinates of Isabela's volcanic graveyards being misinterpreted as an all-encompassing true destination—the place where the drones would land and a bright light would go off in their circuitry and their task would be marked as completed forever. Approximately 0.17% of the Earth's drone population passed close enough to the Galápagos to be affected by this glitch, and half of that percentage had received an updated firmware that rendered it harmless. Over the course of a year, 204,332 drones landed on Isabela. After they landed, they didn't lift up again. Soon stacked atop each other, their landing sensors interpreted the towers of drones as uneven terrain, and they oriented themselves at the cleverest angles to prevent them from damaging the "ground." The drones made a procedurally generated structure on the last stabs of the Galápagos that jutted from the ocean.

0.06% of the global drone population gone missing was too small of a percentage for the humans to get concerned or curious. The species had more pressing business to handle, like the mountain of interrelated problems their ancestors had been happy to leave as a parting gift. Until a marine biology student named Achanqara, bored from working on her thesis, decided to check the satellite imagery off the coast of her hometown of Guayaquil. She was the first human to witness the drones' resting place, the interconnecting circles they had built across their sliver of island, their shining plastic heads of white and gray and black. Achanqara immediately told everyone, and yet the humans weren't quick enough to see it themselves. By the time enough resources were free to stage a small expedition, the drones' navigation glitch had been patched by a group of East African programmers who had taken it on as good coding practice. The drones awoke and deserted their island in a flock of buzzing motors. Isabela was left in peace.

"Make sure to count your blessings," Aunt Charlotte muttered, "because your Grandma being dead is certainly one of 'em."

Prisca snorted, moving her checkers piece a row forward. She was engaging with a fragile stack of virtual overlays while sprawled in the ATV's backseat. Even though Prisca was playing on a physical, portable checkers board, her aunt's side of the game was beamed in all the way from the northern tip of the Appalachians, resulting in occasional lag. Aunt Charlotte's hologram sat up with a huff, crossing her arms.

"I'm not joking, girl! She's doing pirouettes in her grave at the very least. You're out here melting into your galoshes every day to resurrect a *bank?*"

Prisca peered from their parking spot in the shade, swamp sprawled to the horizon. Asmara stood deep in the muck, just like when they first came out here to teach the kids, though his eyes glazed over with the HUD of a long-distance call. He was enduring an informal check-in from the soil union, judging from the amount of sighing going on over there.

"It wasn't a bank," Prisca said, shifting back to the game. "It was an insurance company."

"Don't tell me there's m□ch of a difference."

"I'm not here to convince you to like my projects, auntie. I'm here to beat yo□ in the next five ro□nds." She hopped over a few virtual checkers pieces. "Besides, like I said, resurfacing the structure's not to recreate the past. It's to make it something new, something useful. You'd rather our history dissolve?"

"There's a whole lot of history I'm not eager to claim."

"Fair," Prisca said. But she hadn't stopped thinking of the Mutual Tower since Earth had hit her with the revision note, imagining the concrete building beneath the swamp water like a hulking creature.

"It's Black Wall Street. North Carolina Mutual Life Insurance started not far from here in the late 1800s, auntie. It helped make this one of the few places where we could build."

"They really slapped 'Black' on it and thought it'd make a difference."

"Please don't be like that. It's not literally Wall Street."

"B□t it s□re as hell was capitalism." A□nt Charlotte h□ffed, pointing a finger at Prisca like the hologram co□ld provide tactile feedback and poke her niece in the shoulder. "This what I'm talking about, see? Poor Mom would've died all over again to hear you speak like this."

If only her family could have channeled their penchant for dramatics into acting. Instead, Prisca had to juggle a legacy of bickering teachers, librarians, and activists.

"People aren't gonna read a few plaques, take a small tour and then be swayed by the remnants of a fallen civilization to bring back fossil fuels and become landlords or whatever," Prisca said. "They're smart, and I'll teach them."

"Teach them what?"

Asmara began stomping back to the ATV. Prisca packed up the checkers board in preparation for when he hopped behind the wheel.

"How about you be the one thing in my life to gimme some time and think on it? I'll call yo□ later to finish □p the game. Love you."

Aunt Charlotte faded out, promising more chastising and a rematch, and Asmara took her place. He slumped into the seat beside Prisca, eyes barely open. Without a word, they swapped seats. Prisca started up the vehicle and steered them out.

"So that wasn't a great call, I assume."

"Something like that," Asmara said. "More deadlines, fewer resources. They're iffy about extending your term as delegate because they want everyone in the community to get their time. But we'll get it. At least the months we need to lift your damn tower out the ground."

"Man do I hope it'll only be a few months."

"You know what? Let's just not talk about it. I challenge us to a drive with no work things."

"Love it."

They trudged back home. Partway back to town, Asmara fell asleep. It had to have been the ATV's rocking that did him in. As dusk settled, Prisca switched on the headlights, grateful that they didn't outshine the stars. A glimmering net emerged from the sun's pink. Prisca wondered how the planet might have watched them then. As per Asmara's challenge, she wouldn't think of work. Only of the path filled with screeching bugs, the heat that clung to her back, and the whir of the vehicle she trusted to bring them home.

Prisca mistook many of the lights they passed in the night for the planet's unblinking eye.

Kola is a writer and new media artist/scholar from Durham, NC. He st□dies how different societies engage with and create virt□al spaces. Yo□ can find his work in *Strange Horizons*, *COMPOST*, *Blood Knife*, *FIYAH Magazine*, and more. There's a full list at https://www.kolaheywardrotimi.com, and you might catch him on Twitter over at @KolaHR.

Snuffing The Night Candles

Scott T. Hutchison

People talking about the phases of the silvery moon,
the Peter Pan brightness beckoning in the stars—
I haven't seen a distant sun in months,
and the fairy tales have shimmered away.
No celestial pin pricks in the darkened cyclorama,
no blazes from back in a time before my tiny self
tried to sparkle into existence. I live in
a perfect night, bundled beneath the
s□ffocation of clo□dy particles
and blankets, an empty visibility
stretching into periphery
and over the horizon.

People love a little star shine.
I don't know what happened
to me. I'm anchor-chained on this stark lake
of arrogance and folly, a slow lapping without
the benevolence of illumination
and godsend.

A child wishes
on the first one she sees, lovers wish
on the fallen—I have no blessed light
to witness. Something cheerlessly cast out
has happened here. What America
coughs up to heaven
might be what happened. Of course
I want answers. I pray someone
has the heart
to wish for the future,
for me.

Scott T. Hutchison's previous work has appeared in *The Georgia Review* and *The Southern Review*. Poems are forthcoming in *Appalachian Heritage, Pine Mountain Sand & Gravel*, *Evening Street Review, Narrative Northeast,* and *Naugatuck River Review*. A new book of poetry, *Moonshine Narratives*, is available from Main Street Rag Publishing.

Sold for Parts

Nicole Bade

Cheena's so quiet, she never talks anymore after her shifts. She just comes home and puts her clothes away. Drapes herself in a white sheet, tied like a toga, doesn't worry about anything hanging out or staying in. It's the shape the toga makes against her thighs that matters to her. The strong edges and the void covered by cloth. I wonder if it's true what they say, that someone threatened to take her breath and she stopped using it for anything but motion, like it was something you could horde. Either that, or Cheena doesn't think words have meaning anymore. So we sit next to each other on the sofa and watch a few shows on the net, until it's time for my shift and Cheena sleeps.

I have the opposite of Cheena's job, so our professions are related. I clean up after the party's over. Put the glass back in the windows, toss the hors d'oeuvres and return lost garments. If there's a fight on the net, I weigh in. But mostly, no one fights anymore. It's like they're all too afraid to say what they think because it might lead to the things we'd all rather not think about. The company's been running for a decade and it used to be all high-end space station parties, trips to Mars and endless flights to China, Iceland, Algeria. Now people come to us. They want something that doesn't change. And I always put the room back the same way.

Cheena was gonna be an astronaut before the deal. But it wasn't the deal that made her silent. As for me, I talk enough for both of us and more than I should. I hang out on the threads that still try to list the disappearing animals. I'm responsible for spotting five kinds of insects, seven mammals and three reptiles. When they're gone, I'll watch new ones, until they're gone too. One man's job is to watch the mountains. Two are still there, but the range is all hollowed out. Desert now. We don't talk on the thread about why they're gone. No one can stomach that, and we don't want to hope too hard. Life is livable a little bit at a time.

I was a scientist before the deal, but I can't remember any of it anymore. Not one equation. They tell me I'm better to talk to now. That I was always a little haunted or analytical or something. Now

I can't stop talking. I talk to the bots that help me reshape the rooms of the floating castle. I talk to the other staff, the bartenders and the talent. I talk to Cheena, even though she doesn't say a word. It's an unspoken agreement that she doesn't have to respond. At work, the music's too loud for anyone to hear her anyway.

I do wish sometimes that I co⊡ld find someone to yell with, to fight, to do anything, b⊡t we all saw what happened to those who panicked that day. And so those of us left just keep on counting the things we loved and took for granted. The things that couldn't change and did. I make the rooms the same every night. Every night Cheena does the same dance. It is what we *can* do.

Nicole Bade is a nonbinary spec⊡lative fiction writer with an MFA in creative writing from Goddard College. In their spare time, they co-curate Two Ho⊡r Transport, a science fiction and fantasy reading series based in Seattle, that welcomes SF/F writers from around the world. Read more about Two Hour Transport at twohourtransport.wordpress.com or on Facebook at facebook.com/twohourtransport.

Their flash fiction story "Strange M⊡sic" was p⊡blished by *Fireside* in April of 2021. You can follow them on Twitter @Nic52165780.

Clama a Dios

Susan Tacent

House at night is quiet despite the insects and bird cries and creatures. Floating in liquid. As if the house were sloshing aro□nd. A container in which fl□id was sloshing. Tidal house. House waves. Amniotic. We cling. We root. We tumble. The sweet gum tree has a greater tolerance for salt than the oak and other hardwoods, and there's the loblolly pine, fast-growing and less susceptible to drought. The house stretches, breathes, sweats. Blood fills the little cracks, ho□se blood, composed of the dreams of everyone who has ever been inside.

Earth is a girl in a short dress. Earth is a girl in trouble. Earth is a girl dreaming of a girl in a short dress in trouble.

"Dad brought home a beagle, Mom."

Say you're a tree with waterfront property, okay, minding your business the way trees do, connected insofar as your roots travel, leafing as needed, barked and bathed in s□nlight or rain, day and night, no different than the rest of □s on this spin-cycle planet. There are pockets and divots and crevices. Everything is shiny or jagged or broken or rough. There are dark places where something might lurk. There are bright places where the light burns. Salinity is bad for trees.

"Can we keep it? Mom, I think we should keep it."

Four homes and a commercial building, brick, that had hosted a variety of retail businesses over its hundred or so years, on Locking Lane. Some historic value but not enough to save them. DeFiore Contractors knocked them down, one, two, three. Salvaging what they could (which wasn't much; some old sinks, copper pipes, wire, a few of the old doors; the bricks from the retailer). One house remained. It would stay, because, unlike the others, its owner was alive. Alice the town clerk who saved the last house was a recidivist smoker and could have lost thirty pounds. The double battle tore at her and made her cranky. But she had just returned from a satisfying lunch, and two half-cigarettes' worth of smoke lingered in her hair. It would be a while before guilt and remorse set in. Guilt, remorse, and disappointment, in herself, her pitiful lack of resolve. She was in the mood to be helpful. In that mood, Alice was formidable.

Earth wakes up. Earth is uneasy now, trembling.

Sea level continues to rise at a rate of about one-eighth of an inch per year.

The apparatus is made of metal. Metal and pvc, which is a kind of hard, durable plastic. There are also plumbing parts, and electronics, which have to do with electricity and motion. The apparatus is not alive. The apparatus is here to serve a purpose.

"The beagle is panting."

"A little."

"Do you think he's scared?"

"I don't know. Maybe, a little."

"Dad's taking forever. I'm going to see."

Describe an egg. Describe all the eggs. Describe any egg. A woman is born with all the eggs she'll ever have.

Grandma suddenly told a story. "We were on a date. And the bridge. It was a drawbridge. That was about to open. It was snowing. Danny instead of stopping just as the what-is-it-called the blockade the thing that is supposed to prevent cars from passing goes down, he g⊡ns it and off we go over the bridge which had already begun opening and whomp"—she did a whomping smack on the table with her hand, rattling the dishes—"we landed on the other side. Fishtailed a little. It was snowing. Forecasts weren't accurate back then." "You told me to go," Grandpa said, downing the last of his drink. Grandma went white. Down went the fork. Grandma said, "Yes, but why? Why did I do that?" "We were in love," Grandpa said. Then he started coughing. Then it was night.

Tree, what do you wish for? We want that wish too.

Life is a mask we assume human form. Coldblooded doesn't mean their blood is cold.

Water expands as it warms. Ice melts.

Where can a fella get a drink these days?

Earth is a boy in a short dress. Earth is a boy in trouble. Earth is a boy dreaming of a boy in a short dress in trouble. Earth is awake. Trembling. Is Earth a mountain?

Eight of the world's 10 largest cities are near a coast. Oceanfront property is the dream scenario. Realtors claim this is true.

Hours before Great-Aunt Lillie died she asked for a cigarette. It had been thirty years since the last one and she was ninety-nine if she was a day. Oh god so good, she didn't say, didn't have to, you could see it in her eyes and the whoosh of that long hard suck of dirty air. Elena the hospital nurse climbed on a chair and unscrewed the smoke alarm, swathed in scrubs like an angel.

Living in a floating city feels a bit like being a soap b□bble in a warm bathtub, or a little rowboat snug on its tether, or like tiptoeing on soft carpet. We rely on meclazine and ginger ale to counteract varying degrees of motion sickness but agree it's far better than living in the reg□lar old cities where basements flood, salt marshes turn to sand, and cars rust from the chassis up.

The floating city is home to a very small percentage of the overall population, including nonhuman animals, who seem to have adapted beautifully. We know how lucky we are but not why and there's no one to ask. Maybe it doesn't matter. We woke one day and there we were. First thing, we voted to keep the whereabouts of o□r floating city a secret. Really we had no choice. Even if yo□ managed to find □s, where in heaven's name wo□ld we p□t yo□.

Sperm met egg. Knock knock. Who's there. Me. Me who. Me I don't know no one's named me yet. Sperm penetrated egg wall. Wiggly ambassador to giant host, round as a planet. Knock knock. Who's there. Tickled. Tickled who. Me, that tickled me. Sperm embedded, cozy as an indoor cat on a cold wet night. Set in motion, life began.

On the drive back from the funerals they get behind a line of vans each with a sticker that reads En Caso de Emergencia, Clama a Dios." Why would they make a joke about that?" Sal says after they translate for her, indignant as fuck. "Maybe it's not a joke," Mom says.

Sources

As Sea Levels Rise, So Do Ghost Forests, Moises Velasq□ez-Manoff and Gabriella Demczuk, *New York Times*, 10/08/2019

NOAA. Is sea level rising? National Ocean Service website, https://oceanservice.noaa. gov/facts/sealevel.html, 11/05/2020

Susan Tacent's work appears or is forthcoming in *Tin House Online, Michigan Quarterly Review, Blackbird, DIAGRAM, Slice Magazine, Coolest American Stories 2022,* and elsewhere. In addition to teaching writing workshops for her local public library and Creature Conserve, a nonprofit that celebrates, st□dies, and protects animals and their environment by bringing artists, writers, and scientists together, she feels lucky to facilitate a lively assisted living book club, seven years strong now, where the participants' collective age exceeds 900 years.

We dreamt once,

Jessica McDermott

in unison,
the wind beating the fence
surrounding the giant intaglios, where
you told me there was nowhere to step
anymore, that the whole
desert started miraging as a geoglyph.

And what was lost
before by time
or destruction returned

in the form of a man etched
on the desert floor,
and you chose
two lucky stones to take home
to remember the black desert—
the Area of Critical Environmental Concern
you read about on the placard that pictured
where we stood
from space.

Driving back home,
saguaros peaking the freeway
beside legions of stucco houses
like a popup book

you turned to say maybe we *should* still have kids,
and I said maybe the desert would last to greet them.

Blyth, California, November 2020

Jessica McDermott is place-based nat□re writer and a fifth-generation Idahoan. She received her MFA in creative nonfiction writing from the University of Idaho in 2016. Along with writing poetry and personal essays, she has published articles on environmental and political issues. She lives in So□thern California.

Enclosures

paulo da costa

By the hand of your great-uncle Zé and great-aunt Fernanda, you and your sister Amari enter the enormous bird enclosure. The cackle begins. The geese do what they do best, warn those inside and those one hundred metres around the farm that intruders have arrived. The sound is deafening. The peacocks join the chorus. You inspect the clay roost lined with straw, where the chickens lay their eggs.

"How many, Koah?"

You shrug, disappointed. There are none to collect.

The daily visits to the farm and to the animals offer you a type of informal schooling that no longer exists in this neighbourhood. You are the last student of this farmland, entering the pens, cages, coops to play with the animals, or running across the fields to inspect the bugs that hide under scattered implements. No other child is seen holding a ladybug on the palm of a hand, or sticking twigs into the mole's underground tunnels, hoping to stir one out of its hide-and-seek game.

In these five months in Portugal you are becoming fluent in more than another human language to aid you in relating with different cultures. You are also learning to converse with the animals, the trees and the stones. You are listening to those who will soon be killed and eaten, and learning about the violence of the world. This is a place where the pigs hang by their hind legs, splayed at the spine like crimson books in butcher windows. At the end of our road, the suckling ones are a delicacy on a spit. The price of one euro per kilo is offensively low for a life, if there ever was a fair price for death.

Great-uncle Zé walks you around the little cement pond. Ducks race in laps, motored by their orange paddles, pretending it is not another typical day of mayhem. The blend of mud and fowl droppings, its squish, squish, arrests your steps. You stare at your once flashy green runners. Sighing, you carry on. The raft of ducks makes no waves until you arrive at the rectangular wooden bird house on stilts, home to the Pekin bantams. Then the ducks also quack up their own storm. You crawl and disappear inside the deep and narrow hens' house too short even for your four years. Moments later you hold a tiny bantam egg. Your palm opens and closes, feeling the small frail shell.

The striking white feathers of the pheasant distract us from the ruthless beak that last week killed a Helmeted guinea fowl, and a peacock several times his size. The strong farm arms of your great-uncle Zé lift you to where, balanced and woven against a grapevine, baby pigeons chirp in their nest.

"We leave those babies be, Koah," Uncle Zé tells you, as your hand stretches out to touch the nest.

Iridescent in the light, the nest shines from the blue-green peacock feathers collected to decorate it. The mother pigeon flies frenetically about the enclosure. Other pigeons fly in and out through the small gaps in the wire ceiling. These are racing pigeon refugees from the neighbour; birds no longer capable of earning their keep in medals or pride. They now seek shelter, easy food and company amid the larger family of winged ones.

This is the same uncle who decades ago invited me and the neighbourhood children for an afternoon of killings in the orchard. Hosts of sparrows had been pecking at the cherries, irritating him and other neighbours also at war with the hungry birds competing for their favourite fruits.

I remember wounded sparrows, wings broken by shots of the pellet gun, flapping sideways on the grass. I remember sparrows missing an eye, frozen in shock, blood trickling down the neck, the soft grey feathers in my hand staining red. I have never stopped remembering.

I stayed at a distance as the other houndlike boys raced after the fired shot and fetched the wounded creatures, who remained very still in the grass, stunned by fright, pain or by the smell of death. The boys collected the quasi-dead sparrows and strung them by the feet, twenty to a twine, a cascade of death that hung from a post as a warning to other winged creatures. Including their ineffective guardian angels.

The neighbourhood boys and your great-uncle Zé proceeded to pluck the feathers from the tiny sparrows after they had been immersed in the stockpots of boiled water. This was the boys' initiation into a mass killing that apparently had been a pastime in your great-uncle's childhood. He sang the praises of the delicacy to come as a reward for the hard work of the afternoon soldiers: a well-earned tomato-rice bird stew. I remained a little behind the eager boys, chopping onions. My lips were clenched.

During the extended dinner preparation, great-uncle Zé entertained the boys with tales of ambushes, exotic snake attacks and night guerrilla battles during his time in a West African war, one of the bloodiest Portuguese colonial battles. Within fourteen years, in Guinea-Bissau, ten thousand conscripted soldiers lost their lives, and one hundred thousand Africans lost theirs. Many young Portuguese men fled the country to avoid the draft. Your underage great-uncle Zé was an eager early volunteer, later returning with a 'love' tattoo for his regiment on his forearm.

When the dinner call arrived, I did not sit at the long table of twelve. Hearing the tiny bird-bones crunching inside the joyful mouths of the other children served as the conclusion to that story. That was the afternoon I became a non-meat eater in my mind, although it took two more decades before it became daily practice.

The goats bleat; they recognize your voice in the distance. We climb the knoll to the upper fields where they await. In heat, the buck reeks. My eyebrows rise. You do not seem to mind the gallant's choice of perfume. The goats press their bodies to the double wire fence that cannot prevent their heads from squeezing through. They stretch their tongues to reach for the deep green collard in your hand. After an hour of back and forth snapping collard leaves from the field, you lie down on the grassy ditch next to the fence and converse with the four-legged. I cannot hear what you say. Goats stare and listen, despite the lack of collard in your hands. Once in a while, the large male or the baby bleats.

You are learning about the imprisonments that condition the free movement of beings, and how a prison also conditions the guards, who can never live far from the fences themselves. One day, you will learn that this profession is still called husbandry, a practice rooted in domesticating and controlling the lands and its non-human creatures. And one day, a little or a lot later, you may choose to have a woman companion that convention will call a 'wife'. Then you may want to question the links, the meanings *encooped* in these words, in these practices, and also choose not to be husband to a wife. Or a husband to a husband.

While you feed the goats collard leaves, your great-aunt Fernanda arrives with a glimmer in her eye. "Come." You giggle and follow her; you appreciate surprises. It takes all your might to control the pace of your steps and remain behind your great-aunt. In the kitchen, by the fireplace, sits a shoebox. Ti Fernanda opens it. Piu . . . piu . . . . Your eyes widen to the fluffy chick inside, born just hours ago. The bird cowers and attempts to hide in the corner of the shoebox.

"You can pick her up, Koah," great-aunt Fernanda encourages.

You are not so sure.

"Where's the mamma?"

"It doesn't have a mamma."

You do not believe her.

A dish, the size of a jar lid, has overturned inside the shoebox, scattering gritty cornmeal feed. The bird burrows under the thin layer of wood shavings cushioning the shoebox.

Your great-aunt cups her hands, lifts the chick up. The bird attempts to jump. A fall on the hard tile could break her toothpick-thin legs. Ti Fernanda passes the bird to your cupped hand. Your index finger runs over the bald and bony head no larger than your thumb, then caresses the yellow fuzz on her wing. A combination of tenderness and awkwardness, since the bird wants to walk out of your hand, and you are unsure how to handle this fragility asserting her own will.

After a time, the fast-pulsing chest suggests a stressed bird. I propose walking outside to see the goats. You stay a moment longer, kneeling by the box, watching, talking to her with the tenderness of a father loving his own offspring.

Another day has passed. I steer you to the goats' fenced field and avoid walking near the kitchen. Your great-uncle Zé tells me the chick dehydrated, forgotten in front of the heater.

When you ask about the newborn chick, I mumble about it

not being in the kitchen any longer. You know it is an excuse, yet you ask nothing more. There is another side to your great-aunt and -uncle that you do not yet see or understand. It is a paradoxical equation of affections. For all the incommensurable love Ti Fernanda and Ti Zé show you, there is also their unconscious side, in neglecting their farm animals. I don't know why I believe I must wait for another time to explain best the unintended or intended cruelty of those who are close to us. The most difficult affections, you will learn, will be when love and harm intersect. Some of your deepest hurts in memory will likely come from me, since I have already provided you with your first disappointments, anger, and conflicts.

Sometimes those who love us are willing to listen, and even willing to change because of our emotional gravitational pull in their lives. You grandfather Agosto stopped caging birds after a few years of listening to my unhappiness at seeing the birds in captivity. I suggested he could also enjoy them flying about in the sky and yard. He would fall silent and stare at the caged birds. One day I arrived from Canada to find the bird enclosures not only empty, but also dismantled.

"They are never far, anyway," he told me, pointing out a nest in the tall ornamental cedar beside us. In the ensuing quiet, the chirping of baby *melros* trickled down. Soon, a mother darted in with a wriggling worm on her beak.

Your grandfather smiled.

On arriving in Portugal, you cringed upon seeing chained dogs barking frantically from their tiny cement doghouses. "Why does Ti Zé tie them up? Why is that second dog barking so madly at me?" After a few weeks you have begun to accept their neurotic condition, and to imitate your great-uncle, who taught you to use an osier twig to strike Bolinhas, eliciting compliance for sitting and rolling on the lawn.

There is a tale of two chained dogs on your great-uncle Zé's farm. Bolinhas, a recently acquired puppy, lives in a cement doghouse next to the raven's now empty cage. This Labrador belongs to Ti Zé's granddaughter, who lives in Brussels. She requested a puppy to play with twice a year on her Christmas and summer visits. Willing to please his granddaughter, Ti Zé unchains Bolinhas to run off-leash in the yard most days and feeds him store-bought dog food and treats, while the twelve-year-old mutt Caima, two chain lengths away on the other side of the link fence, looks on, and sniffs the drifting air. His bones mimic the ribcage of a disintegrating caravel. Never off his chain, Caima watches from the adjacent muddy field. Any time we bring the veggie scraps from grandmother Micas' house to feed Ti Fernanda's sheep, we also carry a bowl of left-over soup, chicken bones and day-old cornbread for Caima. He yaps and wags his tail. It is not every day we have leftovers.

You are learning about human incoherence, witnessing that some affections are narrow, selective, leaving the heart blind to others. It is a roulette of fortune. The ball seldom lands twice on the same lucky number. That is why, when the sun shines on us, it is essential to be grateful for privilege and not be blinded by self-absorption. In those moments, it is kind to look around, seeking those who need the warmth and have been confined to the shadows.

Ti Zé and Ti Fernanda are not conscious of the harm they inflict on animals, having been born into farming practices carried out for centuries. The absence of day-to-day moral dissent also permits unchallenged behaviour to flourish. You and I are also at the mercy of our cultural blindness, and it is our obligation to peel away such blinds to make our choices free from obvious social and cultural conditioning. You hold significant emotional influence over those around you, as they are willing to hear and please you. They want your happiness, and will expand that circle of care to others, if you so insist.

I encourage you to speak your worries about the chained dogs to Ti Zé.

You do.

He laughs.

You don't.

Ti Zé does not know what to tell you. It is the way he has lived his life with farm animals. By domination. Punishment. Their servitude. He once shot his dog in anger for biting him when he struck the dog with a hose for having disobeyed a command. It will take another trillion raindrops to change the shape of a stone that believes its present form is all it can be. Patience is the most difficult practice for those who do not have a thousand years to live, those witnessing animals already dying every day from neglect and abuse.

Patience is difficult for those of us recognizing another's pain.

Day after day, following the slowness of the seasons, you have already grown to understand the necessary courage to make this world a better place. Yet, the one who names the injustice while standing among those benefiting from that injustice becomes vulnerable, often triggering redirected wrath.

I look forward to you growing older, even more articulate and assertive, and bringing to light the numerous, varied enclosures in my mind. I hope to be grateful, while dismantling such mental cages, to free the possible dreams still invisible to me. That day will mark the beginning of another journey, one more reciprocal, in the learning exchange between us.

It is our last week in the valley, and you are turning stones on a field, looking for worms, finding snails instead, which you roll on your hand to inspect.

When you attempt to separate a snail from its shell, I explain that the snail will die without it, and since it is attached, it would likely be as painful as tearing your arm from your body. You move your attention on to the glistening black slugs in collard paradise. I harvest sweet-smelling tangerines from a wooden ladder propped against the roof tiles on the herb-drying building.

I have only collected a dozen tangerines in the bag when you arrive.

"Paulo, Paulo."

In your hand you hold a tiny snail. Its broken shell reveals a hole the size of your thumb. Your face tells me that you are upset.

"Will it die?"

"It might. A shell doesn't grow back. Small and fragile creatures depend on our gentleness."

You become silent, staring at the snail you have returned to the ground. It is not moving.

I have seen or heard the perishing stories of the animals in this farm. From territorial fowl that should not be sharing crowded enclosures to sheep without their water replenished on scorching days, from infirm ostrich, rabbits, or chickens to an ailing, gaunt mare meeting his last moment, the plethora of agonies are endless.

The animals are ornamental objects Ti Fernanda and Ti Zé

dream up for their vision of a farm. The creatures become living toys to entertain grandchildren and other visitors. Your great-aunt and uncle fail to see farm animals as feeling beings who suffer and require the love, attention and care dispensed to you and your sister. Fernanda and Zé's perennial struggle to remain within the limits of accomplishable farm tasks in a day costs these incarcerated creatures their lives. The animals cannot help themselves and will live or die at the mercy of an unreliable hand.

You do not yet know that it breaks your mother's heart to walk into this farm, yet she does not let her sadness diminish with your joy in your interaction with the animals. This farm is a playpen for you, but an animal concentration camp for us.

Since childhood Ti Fernanda and Ti Zé have been my favourite aunt and uncle for their generosity, playfulness, spontaneity and good disposition. Despite contradictions and my ethical and moral divergence, they continue to be dear to me as they already are dear to you. It is a tense cliff edge at times. They understand where my values clash with theirs. In our complex web of human and family affections, we hold this reality: a great-aunt and -uncle who can be ignorant of the suffering they cause.

We teach you that this or any other farm's existence is not a validation, much less an endorsement, of an animal's natural fate. Month by month, year by year, we will teach you to see beyond the veneer of appearances, and to read between the lines, seeking the missing narratives. Ignorance can carry on for eternities, like sadness and its acceptance. How we treat those vulnerable is an elemental matter to our higher consciousness and will reflect our core being. We will be defined not only by what we choose to create, but also by what we refuse to destroy.

Today is April 25th, Revolution Day. The Portuguese celebrate deposing a fascist government that ruled the country for forty years, until 1974, the year Aunt Marina was born. I was nine years old. The image I retain most vividly replays an old woman in black scurrying along the cobblestone road shouting, "The revolution has arrived, the revolution has arrived. Olive oil is going down to *cinco tostões* a bottle now, five cents. *Viva a Revolução*!" Olive oil's price increased every year thereafter. It is two hundred times more expensive today and no longer the cooking staple of the working people. It has been substituted in their kitchens by imported sunflower oil. Not only had the people become free that day, the market had also. The median wage has risen a mere fourteen times since that April day. More importantly, a myriad other essential gains, from education to health, have been achieved, and every citizen is free to complain now, meaning that political imprisonment or torture is no longer permitted.

This holiday afternoon we prepare to visit the cousins from your grandfather's side of the family in the neighbouring county of Oliveira. Their semi-rural, three-house cluster holds nine people. Their extended clan across three generations of committed hobby-farmers grows most of their vegetables and fruit, animal flesh and herbs.

Every year, our cousins effusively receive you and Amari. In fine Portuguese-hospitality style, a banquet of home-baked sweet cakes and breads awaits us, including vegetarian dips and healthy options for the odd Canadians we are. They believe the non-meat inclination is a generalized Canadian trait, not our fringe family preference.

The cousins immediately take you and Amari to visit the two dozen rabbits they raise in cages. You pet them and their babies. No one tells you the rabbits are food. A dinner plate destiny for these long-eared, fuzzy creatures does not cross your mind. When I look at those rabbits, a deep stomach knot reaches back to my childhood. Every Saturday, I accompanied my father, often with my mother, to your great-grandfather Manuel da Costa's farm in the village of Vermoim, over the Cambra hills. That is where I met these second cousins weekly, and we played in terraced fields and back woods. Several times a year I watched your grandfather Agosto kill and prepare a rabbit for the Sunday roast the following day, a special lunch to reward the long work week.

On one of those Saturday afternoons, your grandfather selected the plumpest rabbit from the wooden cage and brought the buck dangling from hind legs to the cement washing tank. The water gurgled in a continuous stream, overflowing to a channel that irrigated the cornfields down below. In the past some rabbits had squirmed and sprung, resisting what they must have smelled was their approaching end. Others dangled, resigned, or perhaps frozen in fear. Beneath the hanging pigeon house and the cooing birds, vovô Agosto would hold the rabbit upside-down. A swift hack of his hand to the rabbit's neck was as good as an axe. The strike aimed to fracture the rabbit's spine, to instantly kill. Two or three strikes sufficed.

The smack, smack, smack, echoed against the tender splash of water flowing from the black plastic pipe that brought cool water from the spring on the hill, several hundred metres above. The two pigeons stopped their cooing at the first strike of bone on bone.

With unease, I watched the fear in the rabbit's eyes intensifying after the first strike, its springing legs attempting to hop away from the nightmare, yet finding no ground beneath. Your grandfather struggled to aim the next strike at the neck, now made more difficult by the wildly swinging rabbit in his grasp. He clenched his lips, not enjoying the task.

At the third strike, the rabbit became motionless. Your grandfather tied its hind legs with a cord and dangled the rabbit from the two knobs on the double door. The white, soft belly faced us. A couple of quick slices along the heel revealed muscle, allowing a hold for your grandfather's fingers to pull off the rabbit's fur coat in a steady, loud rip. The first tear echoed in the still air of the hot afternoon as the rabbit began to violently swing from the wall. The carpal bone strikes of the hand had only stunned the rabbit to unconsciousness. I screamed. Your grandfather turned pale.

"Stop. He is alive."

"They're only muscle spasms," your grandfather tried to assuage me.

Blanch-faced, he continued ripping the fur to end everyone's agony sooner. The rabbit stopped jerking after a few seconds, succumbing to the pain of being skinned alive, having woken up from one horror to experience another far worse.

You cradle your cousin's rabbit against your chest. It kicks, wanting to hop away. The jostle frightens you. You move on to visiting the chickens and stomp in their fenced yard, attempting to catch one, cautioned not to step on their droppings. A car zooms past on the nearby road and the song that symbolizes the revolution, played today on every radio and TV, drifts away with it. "Grândola Vila Morena" always makes me think of your other great-aunt Fernanda, imprisoned and tortured while in the resistance movement, and whose mental health, after release, was never the same. I had planned for you to finally meet her on this trip, while showing you Coimbra, the city of my university years; however, she died days before we landed, having choked on her breakfast, alone in the bedroom of her old age home.

We leave the chicken coop and stroll in the vegetable garden. Your Bustelo cousins tenderly lift you off the ground to reveal the three wild nests of *melros* and serin finches concealed among the dense foliage of their pear and apple trees. They leave them be.

After indulging in the afternoon feast disguised as a humble snack, we all stroll along a fallow field. A ladybug lands on your chest, a butterfly on your shoulder. You hold the ladybug on your open palm until it flies away. We soon say goodbye to our relatives, carrying home armfuls of arugula, lettuce, watercress, collards, cabbage, fresh lemon balm for tea, dill and oregano herbs. This green bounty will feed us for days.

On our return home from Bustelo, you want to squeeze in a visit to the goats and the sheep. Hoping to drop leftovers to Caima, you are disappointed when grandmother Micas says there are none today. The sun slides down the horizon, assailed by the cutting wind from the north. We are at the end of another Revolution Day. My mention of returning to the apartment, a three-hundred-metre walk from Ti Fernanda's farm, prompts a sudden wave of tiredness, and you cannot drag one foot in front of the other.

I attempt to motivate you.

"Tomorrow is the start of your last week in school, Koah."

"Paulo, school is boring. We sit most of the day."

I understand. For the first time in your life you are experiencing entrapment. It is apartment life, in winter, at the busiest intersection of this small city; it is the lack of lushly treed parks; but mostly it is the confinement to four walls in school, for five weekdays. All of this is a new way of living after playing in the spacious green spaces, forests and shores of Victoria. You want to escape walls as a bird wants to escape a cage.

You have not been conditioned to stillness, hypnotized by screens, or inured to confined living spaces. You want your day to continue in your grandparents' yard or your great-aunt's farm across the lane. Domestication is a word you have yet to learn, although you smell its approach. That is also why you do not sleep under a blanket. Even in your sleep, the lightest bed sheet covering you is kicked away. You want no pressure, no weight upon your dreams.

We stroll down to where the lane joins the larger road leading to our apartment. At the corner, in the house with many pets, the effusive parrot greets you, "Olá". You match his high-pitched screech with a returning "Olá". You stop, lean over the spiked railing to talk, and admire the bird scratching his grey, feathery torso with his unchained leg. He walks sideways in frenetic steps along the stick-perch, excited to see you, pleased with your attention.

We finally begin moving again and are within sight of the apartment when we hear the cry of a bird in the sky. The insistent and long song accompanies the last droplets of light.

"Spring must be near, Koah."

That is when you begin singing:

A seagull flew, flew
wings of wind,
heart of the sea.
Like her, we are free,
we are free to fly

My heart stops. You sing it freely and lightly. Acquainting you with the sounds of Portuguese while in the womb every night, I sang you this verse. I am surprised and unsure how you have memorized the words. You do not know the political context of this song, yet. I sang you revolutionary freedom songs from '74 to welcome you into the world. What you do not yet know is that the people of Portugal borrowed the images of free animals, such as the gull in our ocean-kissed country, to inspire them to attain their own freedom. Now that the Portuguese people are freer than they were in my childhood, it is time to extend the favour to others who are not free: the animals still incarcerated in our midst.

Nearing the apartment, on our last week in the valley, you slow down our progress by first walking backwards, then testing your balancing skills and walking on the long, thin wall of another apartment complex. You pretend to be an acrobat probing your limits. Then without warning, you jump down from the wall like the kid you are.

"We have to free the goats, papá. Once we are gone to Canada, they need to be able to get the collards on their own."

"You are right, Koah. I'll let Ti Zé know."

"Please don't forget." You say it with your most serious face.

"I will certainly not."

You carry on along the wall, hopping up and down, until you stop and turn to me, full of conviction.

"And the chickens too need to be freed," you conclude, adding a determined nod.

It is another April, four decades after carnations plugged the barrels of machine guns, and the revolution is yet to arrive at the enclosures of those animals we have used as inspiration for action in art and song. We are the jail keepers and dictators we believed we had freed ourselves from. Perhaps the April revolution will mature alongside you and your sister, as you run through the sandy Furadouro beach and dive into the Atlantic, seeking the perfect surf. The wave will curl up, almost shy, just before unravelling its power. It will propel you far and wide. Then the seagulls, flying freely above the sailing boats, will join you, singing their song.

Born in Angola, and raised in Portugal, **paulo da costa** is a writer, editor and translator living in the Rocky Mountains of Canada. He is the recipient of the 2020 James H. Gray Award for Short Nonfiction, the 2003 Commonwealth First Book Prize for the Canada-Caribbean Region, the W. O. Mitchell City of Calgary Book Prize and the Canongate Prize for short-fiction. His poetry, fiction and non-fiction have been published widely in literary magazines around the world and translated into Italian, Spanish, Serbian, Slovenian and Portuguese. *The Midwife of Torment* is his latest book of fiction.

tied

Ellie Milne-Brown

try to keep yourself—somehow—
tied: to the earth, perhaps—find joints
and sinews that echo your own in
the tree across the water, discover
home in the shelter of hedges or trace
a life down the edges of the river.
please, remember to stay tied:
maybe in her tender touch,
or in the glance shared—across an
expanse or two meters. above all—
i'll keep repeating—be tied: hear the strings
plucked so far away, feel the echo, count
your luck to be here, to be bound, and know
how easy it is to be found.

carcinisation

Ellie Milne-Brown

a comforting thought: that
the arc of the moral universe
is long, but it appears to bend
towards crabs. one day, our
exoskeletons will protect us
from the rain, and from the end;
as the seas rise and fall, we will
find homes in the tide pools, or in
the remnants of buildings left empty
by humans. we will build
a better world, as crabs; they say
crabs can't feel pain. we'll never
hurt, or perhaps we won't believe
convenient claims which salve
our guilt over boiling creatures alive.

Ellie Milne-Brown is a writer and student whose poetry has been featured in *Transcribed: An Anthology of Trans Writing* (Polari, 2020). She recently completed an MA in Gender, Sexuality and Culture, and her time is divided between working in higher education administration, contemplating all the emails she needs to send, and writing a newsletter about the media she loves called *tiny mammal kingdom*.

Rainbow Boy

Amanda Ilozumba Otitochukwu

This story does not begin with my birth; neither does it end with my death, but I will tell you of it regardless for I feel it is important you know of how I left this world in a baptism of blood and oil. Before then, I will tell you what happened in 1958 in Ogoni, Bayelsa state.

PART 1

Brown, marshy mud clings to the bottom of my feet, the dunlop slippers I wear are practically useless, they stick to the mud, making my steps heavy, cumbersome, and each slower than the last. I let out a long sigh as frustration mounts in my chest, bubbling up to my throat and threatening to come out as a scream.

Bassey sees my struggle and begins to laugh." Just commot am," he says, referring to the slippers.

"Oga move along." I push him forward, and he almost slips onto the mud; my grin is unrepentant and his scowl is murderous.

We reach the river after almost an hour of slogging through worm-infested mud and small potholes of water occupied by larvae. At the river, the sweltering heat is even worse, and flies dog o□r every step, their buzzing is irritating and can drive a man to madness if he is not careful. We swat at them when they come too close, only for them to buzz away and come back seconds later. One would think we were corpses with the way they follow us.

The riverbank is like a minefield, only instead of bombs, there are a slew of plastic nylons and bottles, twisted tin cans half-filled with murky water, wood and some other debris too weathered by age for me to make out what they are. I wrinkle my nose and make a mental note to tell Papa that the village needs a clean-up.

One side of the riverbank is occupied by houses made of wood and zinc raised above the water using stilts, and the other side is where the fishermen dock their boats. Bassey and I head there.

O□r fishing boat has already been scr□bbed within an inch of its life and pushed into the edge of the river by Dooh; he waves at us, his hand bobbing in the wind too fast for our eyes to follow. Dooh always has a lot of energy. Bassey and I race to the boat, running the ⊡nspoken competition of first-to-reach; I get there before him and j⊡mp into the boat in a flo⊡rish of tri⊡mph. Bassey drags himself into the boat and plops down on one of the wooden planks for sitting. "I just say make I let you win."

We are the only people on the river today just as Dooh has predicted; the other villagers are celebrating the water festival, so fishing and trading in the market has been p⊡t off for today. It is only one amongst the many festivals our people hold every year; this one is to honour the water spirits that guide our boats as we go to fish; the masq⊡erades wearing headdresses that imitate fish and water birds are my best part of the festival.

I know that by the time we get back to the village, half of the people will be drunk on fermented palm-wine and gin while the others will be tired out from rigorous traditional dances, and those like Bassey will be too full of oily buns and creamy smooth wraps of *agidi* to be able to move.

We would have joined them, but the water festival does not p⊡t food on the table; fishing does.

Dooh nods his head to a song only he can hear, this boy—always singing and dancing. Without much care, he throws our apparatus into the boat one after the other, making it rock and bob violently against the river water. The only thing keeping it from turning over is the combined weight of me and Bassey.

He hands over a net to me, another to Bassey, and holds the last one for himself. Then he throws a wet black nylon at me; I open it to find b⊡ns and *agidi.*

Dooh's mother is one of the women cooking for the village festival; he must have grabbed some of her goodies before coming. I give him a thumbs up, "correct guy." I hail him and take one bun before giving the nylon to Bassey. He wolfs down a wrap of *agidi* in seconds.

After we have satisfied the growling monster of h⊡nger in our stomachs, we untie the boat from the wooden pole that keeps it from drifting into the river. Dooh and Bassey row us past the edge of the river until we reach the swampy area where the river is bordered by thick mangrove vegetation. The tides are low today, making the m⊡dflat dry and visible.

The air here is thick but moist and perfumed by the sickly sweet smell of green vegetation. I lean back into the boat and let my arm hang freely from outside the edge, relishing the feel of cool serene water against my skin. I smile and close my eyes; this is my place. In the open river, I feel free and not weighed down by the daunting responsibility of being the son of the village chief.

The boat comes to a stop and someone kicks my leg. I reflexively jump up, almost falling into the river. Bassey and Dooh burst out laughing. Bassey laughs and wheezes until thick yellow snot rolls down his nose and he has to clean it with the sleeve of his shirt. I hiss and get my net. "Rough play!"

"See the current," Dooh says, "fish go plenty today o."

We nod at him in agreement and get to work. We have done this many times since we were little boys; Bassey arranges the boat's paddle and ties it to the side of the boat with twine, I balance the square boxes we would use to store our catch between the wooden planks in the boat, and Dooh inspects the water. There is no better fisherman team than the three of us.

Bassey opens the box where we stuffed the worms we had caught in the muddy fields before coming. The worms wriggle over each other, their elongated tube-like bodies partially blackened by the mud we hadn't bothered to wash off them. He lifts one in the air and pretends to swallow it. "You're disgusting," I say to him.

"You and your big big English," Bassey sneers. I am the only one of them who speaks *proper* English, I learn from the big dictionary and textbooks Papa buys for me, I think they are a waste of money but Papa says I must read them. He wants me to speak and walk and behave like the white men we see whenever we go to the big city.

I snatch the worms from Bassey's hand and pour them into the water. It does not take long for the fishes to come, they arrive in a frenzy, and if we are not careful, they will be gone with all the worms before we know it—the fish in this area, gluttons!

We spread Bassey's net first and throw it over the water; it billows in the air a little then falls like a blanket, entrapping the fish within its weaving. Then we wait until Dooh signals us to bring up the net—he always knows when it is full. One time; another fisherman called him the fish *Oga*. Dooh's smile that day had threatened to split his face in two.

The net catches a ton of fish just like he predicted, we all let out a whoop, there's even crabs and small crayfish in there. We go again, this time throwing Dooh's net. Mine goes last. It always does.

The sun has already started to descend into the horizon when we decide we have caught enough fish—I and Dooh, anyway. Bassey still wants to get some more. Bassey's Papa and Mama are dead and as the eldest of five, he has to work harder than the rest of us to feed his siblings and put two of them through school in the neighboring community. Sometimes—just like now—his eyes go tight with the strain of how much he works. I pat his shoulders and tell him to rest, I will give him half of my catch to add to his.

In a rare show of affection, Bassey embraces me. "You be my brother for life," he laughs.

He is a head taller than I am, so my face ends up in his sweaty, musty armpits; I gag and push him away in disgust, and Bassey loses his balance and falls into the river with a large splash. My laughter is short-lived as he swims up and pulls me into the water with him. We fight, landing a few playful blows on each other's bellies. Dooh watches from the boat. He does not like to swim—odd for a fisherman, but then again there are many things wrong with Dooh.

He bursts out in a song and a gentle dance. The song is about a boy who has to prove himself as a warrior by fighting an invincible monster. It is a song Dooh composed, and it has somehow become our anthem. Dooh wants to move to the big city and be a singer.

We join him to sing well into the evening; at times like this, we are not fishermen but boys free from the depressing weight of life. Bassey is not an orphan, Dooh is not the man of his family and I am not getting ready to be village chief. We are just three boys no older than fifteen.

PART 2

A helicopter flies overhead; this is the first time we see one fly so close to the village. It is shaped like a giant metal bird. The spinning of its blades causes the trees to bend under the pressure, ripples to form in the water. I marvel at the technology behind the helicopter. I read about them in a textbook; I want to build one someday when I finally leave this village. I say this, but I know it's never going to happen, my people—we never leave. It is as if our souls are tethered to the land.

My eyes follow the helicopter as it flies further into our village. I squint in an attempt to make out the letters painted on it. "S-H-E-L-L D-A-R-C-Y," I spell out loud, then look at Bassey, who shrugs; he is just as confused as I am.

Dooh stops singing and gestures us to come back into the boat, and we do as he says. Somehow, our spirits have been dampened by the helicopter's passing. I cannot help but feel as though it comes with trouble. I shake my head, Papa says I worry too much. That must be it, I agree with my thoughts, but begin to row faster back to the riverbank.

We find Deki—Bassey's little sister—waiting for us there. She holds buns in both hands. Oil drips from her palm and runs down her arm. Bassey gets out of the boat and carries her, he throws her in the air then spins her around. Her squeals are loud and contagious. We all adore Deki, she is so pure and untainted by the strife we have seen in this village, she is the reason Bassey works so hard and she is the reason I let him throw his fishing net first. Deki will leave this village. I want her to because I cannot.

She wobbles to me and pouts with lowered eyes. "Brother Mene won't you carry me too?"

"Why won't I?" I oblige her and spin her around just like Bassey did. Before she is able to ask the same of Dooh, Bassey stops her.

"Wetin you come find for here Deki."

"Erm they're looking for brother Mene," she twists her toes in the sand, a clear sign that that's not the only reason why she's here. The water calls to Deki just like it calls to me, we are kindred spirits so I understand that she cannot help it.

I interrupt before Bassey gets it in his head to scold her, "Who is looking for me Deki?"

"Brother Mene's Papa," she says and skips away like a little imp just as Bassey attempts to grab her. Bassey sighs and says something about how she'll be the death of him someday. The boys agree to go into the city without me, they will sell the fish and bring back my share of money. Meanwhile, I carry the fish we caught for our families and head back into the village, passing by the helicopter on my way.

When I get to the village centre, another villager informs me that my Papa has been searching for me. I wince; if everyone knows then it means he is already angry—Papa's temper can rival that of a bull. I hurry home, stopping briefly at Bassey's and Dooh's houses to drop the fish for their families. Dooh's mother thanks me profusely; I notice the bones in her collar are jutting out more than usual, and the creases in her forehead have deepened.

There are two white men and a boy in the sitting room when I get home.

The boy looks to be around my age, he is dressed in yellow khaki shirt and shorts paired with brown boots—he sits so proper, like a picture, frigid and unmoving. He looks at me, up and down, then turns away, dismissing me as if I hold no interest to him.

My eyes shift to the two men with him. Their faces look weather-beaten and reddened by the sun. I spot a mosquito bite on the nose of the taller one with a camera hanging from his pale neck. I don't know why but it gives me satisfaction because I know the mosquitoes are just starting with them.

Papa and the men finally spot me standing in the doorway. "Mene! where did you carry your legs to?"

"*Sah*, fishing *Sah*," I answer in a rush. Papa waves my answer away and tells me to come sit beside him, he does not even let me rest my bottom fully before he leans into me and begins to whisper in my ear. His breath is hot and stinks of tobacco.

"I don't know what this men are saying, they speak through their nose," Papa complains. I hold back a smile at his genuine frustration. "Talk to them and see what they want! They said something about black gold."

Black gold. Our village—Ogoni—is a swampy, small and remote creek village, so the presence of the white men here is rather strange, and they are here for gold? I know for a fact that there is no gold here. So I scoot forward and address the taller white man, my mind equates height to superiority.

"My Papa says you are here for black gold correct?"

"Yes," he answers, in a nasally tone making me understand

what Papa meant, they really do speak through the nose, but unlike my Papa, it fascinates me. "My name is John by the way; this is William, my son," he gestures to the boy whom I look at dismissively just as he had done to me. "And this good man here is Sunday."

My ears perks up. "That is an unusual name for a white man," I comment; I have never been good at swallowing my thoughts.

"Yes," Sunday answers, "my father named me after his Nigerian friend." I have nothing to say to that so I move on to the black gold.

"This gold, you have proof that it is in our village?"

John nods profusely making sweat fly off his forehead and onto the table that separates us, my eye follows it; so does William's. John continues, "well, black gold is a pseudonym, it is actually oil. Crude oil."

"Oil," I say flatly, trying to sound uninterested as I rack my brain to see whether I have come across crude oil in the textbooks Papa bought for me; sadly, they have only been about aircraft and the white man's etiquette.

"Erm, the oil is deep inside the ground. When we extract it, we can process it and sell it for money, huge money."

Papa sits up at this. It does not matter how a person says it, once money is mentioned, my Papa will understand. The villagers call him money chief behind his back. "Huge money eh now you're talking. This black-gold-oil-something, is it like palm oil?" he asks.

"Exactly, just like palm oil," Sunday says and takes over from John, it is as if they have practiced their speech before coming. "If your village agrees, we will set up oil drills and wells here, don't worry, none of our activities will disturb you people. You wouldn't even notice that we are here."

"Okay, what of the money?" Papa says impatiently. I reach behind him and pat his back so he can calm down. I do not trust these people and I will not let Papa's unhealthy love for money put this village in trouble.

"How do we get the money, I am guessing it is your company that will set up these oil wells, why will you give us money from that?"

Sunday coughs violently into a handkerchief before he answers, "Well, it is your land, so it is only fair we compensate for borrowing your resources, and then we will also employ some of you, boys like you," he says pointing at me. "If all goes without a hitch and we are able to sell the refined crude oil, then the village gets thirty percent of all profits."

"Just how much is thirty percent?"

"You speak very well for a village—er, for a boy living in a rural area," John says. He says it like it is meant to be a compliment but I see the veiled insult within it. They did not expect to meet 'educated' people here.

"Thank you," I utter regardless, "thirty percent?"

"Ah-yes—yes it is a lot of money. It will be enough to develop your village, turn it around. Build a few schools here and there, a hospital too, and a borehole for clean water."

The white man has finally said something that interests me. I lean back and whisper to Papa, explaining all they have said. The boy—William—stands up and announces that he is going back to wait in the helicopter; he stomps out before we can say anything. It is rude, nevertheless it makes me like him a little bit. I often walk out on Papa when he and the other village elders have meaningless meetings.

Papa wants us to agree. "What's the harm there?" he tells me. "We get money, schools, hospitals, and clean water while they get their oil. I don't see how we won't gain for this."

"Okay, but let us not sign any contract yet, I want to see what this black gold is."

"We will agree after we see the oil." Papa pushes me away and tells them. William and John look visibly relieved by our words, as if our disagreement would have been a problem, not for them but for us.

"Come let us show you around our village." Papa gets up and leads the white men out of our house; I follow closely behind.

We take them round the hug of zinc and wooden houses that make our village; the entire village follows us around like an entourage. They titter and gossip; this is the first time most of them are seeing a white man.

"Oyoyoooo see oyibo, see oyibo," they chant as they follow.

The more daring children run up to Sunday and John to shake their hands; Deki is amongst them, she does it and runs back to me huffing and puffing, "I touch his hand," she giggles. I pat her head and send her away. I am becoming more uncomfortable by the second.

John untangles his camera from his neck and begins to take pictures. A click here and a click there. I know what he will do with those pictures later, he will carry them with bare-fisted sanctimony and give to a journalist. The journalist will then do her part as an agent of piety, she will publish the pictures with the headline, STARVING AFRICANS, WE MUST SEND HELP!

Much to my annoyance, the older women put their faces in the camera while the girls smile and wave shyly. The children arrange themselves so that John can snap them one by one. As expected, Deki is first on the line.

Finally, since the whole village is gathered already, Papa decides to announce the reason the white men are here. He tells them of all the benefits we stand to gain by allying our village with John and Sunday's Shell Darcy company. He tells them that they are here for palm oil. I do not bother to correct his misconception, it would be even harder to explain to the villagers.

I blame Sunday for saying it is just like palm oil; I know for a fact that palm oil does not grow beneath the soil and it is neither black nor gold.

The villagers begin to clap and dance and jubilate, they sing and thank the gods for the white men. Someone begins to dole out bottles of gin and leftover *agidi*; the celebration begins anew. I see Dooh's Mama, who suddenly looks full of energy, try to teach Sunday the *Seki* dance. He fails woefully at it. His name might be Nigerian but those dance steps—ah, his feet are not.

I spot Bassey and Dooh and push through the crowd to get to them. "You sold everything?" I ask, surprised they are back so quick.

"Plenty buyers dey today," Bassey replies, "wetin dey happen?"

"The white men say there is oil in our village. They call it black gold and say it will bring a lot of money for us. We will have schools, hospitals and clean water."

Bassey makes a face at the white men. "You dey sure, I no trust them at all."

"Me too," Dooh agrees.

"Me three, but Papa thinks it will be good for the village. I told him to wait until we see the oil first."

"Mene Mene, smart boy! In fact, na man you be," Bassey

praises me, and I smack his head in return.

"Who is that one and why is he there alone, standing like *tambolo* ant?" Dooh turns my head to the opposite end of the village square.

"That is William," I say simply and look away.

Bassey and Dooh give him one last glance before going to seize the opportunity to dance and flirt with girls.

When I turn back again, William is watching them dance with a shadowed frown.

PART 3

In the morning, I am roused from sleep by the lumbering sound of heavy machinery.

The events of last night play over and over again in my head; that's when I remember the white men and their black gold nonsense. I rub at the sleep in my eyes, smearing the yellow mucus between them down the bridge of my nose. Yawning, I fetch a bowl of water and go outside to wash my face, armpits, private area and legs.

Looking up at the sky, I realize that it is barely 6AM, so who and what in the name of everything holy is making such a ruckus this early? "Papa! Papa o!" I yell out for my father but only silence answers me. I go to check his room, expecting to find him still enclosed in a cocoon of sleep but Papa is not there. It seems the noise woke him up before me.

I shut his door and go back to my room where I change into an it-was-white singlet and distressed shorts; my dunlop slippers are by the corner of the entrance still caked in mud. I beat them against the wall outside until the thick clumps of hardened mud fall off, then I put the slippers on and follow the noise until I reach the mud fields. I look down at my feet. Not again, I sigh.

Further down the field, I find Papa and Sunday; they look to be in a serious conversation, which is strange because I know Papa cannot understand anything Sunday says properly. They are surrounded by trucks; these look different from the ones I read about in my books, I'm guessing they are special trucks made for the oil.

"Good morning *Sah*," I greet Papa, "good morning *Oga*

Sunday." John joins us but I don't bother to extend any greeting to him; I have exhausted my fair share of good mornings and the noise of the machinery has made me irritable, I press my fingers against the side of my head as if to push back the headache that is threatening to form there.

I turn to John with a scowl, "I thought you said we would not even notice your presence here."

John chuckles and waves my words away. "Yes yes but this is necessary, it is a one-time thing." He proceeds to explain the process of oil exploration; I am not happy that they have already carried out prior testing on the land without our knowledge but I don't mention it. Instead I wonder when they had the chance to do so that nobody from the village noticed. He tells us not to worry about the trucks, they will soon be out of our way as their target is not the m⊡d fields b⊡t the forest.

The trucks are called thumpers and they are used to create sound waves that will help obtain structural information about the land without drilling a well. It saves time, John adds.

Just then, he signals to the truck drivers and yells over the racket, telling them to cut the engines. The headache in my temple recedes when they do; I let out a sigh of relief. John introduces us to the truck drivers who are engineers, one of them has skin darker than mine, he says he's from Lagos and his team will be arriving as soon as they are done with initial explorations.

The rest of the engineer team consists of men from Britain, Germany and the Netherlands; the men are friendly and easy to talk to. Before I know it, we are joking and jesting while they answer a lot of questions from me about their country. My inquisitive nature has overcome the initial skepticism I felt.

Sunday shows Papa around the trucks, teaching him how to start and move them. The expression on Papa's face is similar to that of Bassey's when we catch a lot of fish. When they are finished, Papa practically skips over to let me know he will be going back home. "The rest of the village will be waking now, I must make sure they don't disturb the white *ogas*."

"Okay, let's go."

"No no, you will go with them, *Oga* Sunday talk say him go show you the oil."

Papa leaves. In his absence I remember William. I don't

know why b□t I begin to search aro□nd the field for him; I find him skulking behind one of the thumper trucks. “Good morning o William how are you today?” I ask with glee in an English I believe is proper and stiff eno□gh for him.

He looks taken aback. “Er good morning Mene.”

“So you even know my name and you pronounced it well too, not like your father and Sunday that pronounce it like they have nails in their mouth.” I expect him to be angry at my jest, but William grins, revealing rows of sharp white teeth and making me see that he is even younger than me.

“I’m sorry about being rude yesterday, I didn’t want to come but father made me.” He shrugs, “I don’t have interest in oil, I think it’s quite messy.”

“It’s okay, my Papa forces me to do some things I don’t like too, I understand.” William tilts his head at me and in that moment, we form an unspoken bond. I let him know he is more than welcome to come fishing with me anytime and he act□ally looks excited by the prospect.

We—I, Sunday, John, William and a woman who appeared out of nowhere—use a boat to cross to the forest while the engineers drive around the river.

The woman holds an umbrella-like thing over her head; it looks familiar, the name it’s called rests on the tip of my tongue but ref□ses to come o□t. I stare and stare at it □ntil finally I tap William to ask, “William, what is the name of that thing?” I say, inclining my head at the woman.

“The thing she’s holding?”

I nod, “I’ve seen it in one of my textbooks but I don’t remember the name.”

“It is a parasol,” he replies. “Women use it to protect themselves from exposure to the sun.”

“Why not just use an umbrella?” I frown.

“The parasol is more ladylike,” William states, matter of fact.

“Oh,” I nod even though it makes no sense to me. The parasol looks like it could be blown away by the slightest breeze, and so does the woman. Lucky for me, I don’t say it out loud, because William tells me she’s Sunday’s wife.

We get to mangrove forest before the thumper trucks do. Once the boat is docked, John wastes no time in exploring, however, the lady stays back in the boat and so does William, making me wonder why they came in the first place.

John points to some areas, then whispers to Sunday. The secrecy makes me feel uneasy, I am about to ask what they are whispering about when something draws my attention.

A tree far off where John had pointed to seems to be shaking; it tilts to one side, and in a yawning split second, the tree falls to the ground. *Gbam.* The tree is followed by another and another and another. For a moment, I am struck silent. Is this an earthquake? But if it is, why do John and Sunday look so relaxed—excited even? Then it hits me.

"What are they doing?" My voice trembles with unbridled anger.

"Why, clearing the area of course, how do you think the trucks and other equipment will get here?" It is John who answers.

"You said nothing about this yesterday!"

"Are you daft boy?"

Ha! These men have the audacity to destroy my forest and ask if I am daft. I fly at John b□t he sidesteps me. "Yo□ said nothing abo□t falling the trees," I yell □sing my finger to hit his chest and punctuate every word. Another tree falls, closer this time; how are they even clearing the trees so fast?

John pushes with more strength than I thought he had; I land on the ground with my bottom, the soft earth breaks my fall. I hear a rustle then a click. When I angle my head up, there is a gun pointed at me. "Our actions here are sanctioned by your government. Do not overestimate your father's authority young man. If we have to use force, then we will."

Sunday lowers John's hand, then comes to kneel beside me. "You do understand that your people never had a choice, don't you?" I nod, bending my head to hide the angry tears that struggle to spill from my eyes. "Go back to the boat, you will be summoned when we find oil."

I stomp away, wondering how to get back to the village to warn my people. Ah! I should never have let Papa agree to this. "William, get out of the boat, you and that woman, now!" Grabbing the oars, I begin to furiously row into the river, not even waiting for them to get out fully.

"I told you it was messy," William says in a hush that rings in my ears all the way back to the village.

The villagers are consumed with outrage at hearing that the white men are destroying our ancestral land, our sacred forest, for oil. They still think it's palm oil. Many of them suggest that the village boys take our boats and go to stop them. Bassey and Dooh are ready to but Papa stops them.

"Papa why now?"

"And lose the money? Think of what it would do for this village and for our people Mene."

"You knew," I say, not a question but a statement, and Papa looks away. The villagers cry out once again, Papa calms them down, filling their heads with promises of better food and water, technology; the entire village is on his side the moment he mentions television. Only a handful of us have seen a television, the screen where people move and talk in, it fascinates them. Even Bassey and Dooh are sold.

It seems I am the only one who does not see any good in this, maybe I am overthinking things as usual, but then I remember the gun John had pointed at my head, I remember Sunday saying our people have no choice. Before I leave, I tell the villagers one last thing. "This people, they will destroy us."

Night time brings the white men back to the village, this time they arrive with more men—some dressed like soldiers. These ones are from Lagos, they treat us the way I expected the white men to. Like rubbish.

The men set up camp at the riverbank in something that looks like a house on a boat; we hear jubilation from their end. They found the oil, lots of it from the sound of things.

The engineer from Lagos comes to invite the village to see samples of the oil they found. My people are quick to light their kerosene lamps, more interested in the merry partying than in the oil.

As village chief, Papa is the first to get to see the oil. There are just two barrels, painted in the same colors as the helicopter, with the same letters, S-H-E-L-L D-A-R-C-Y, written in yellow just below the opening of the barrel.

Papa dips his right hand up to his elbow into the barrel and draws it out, the Lagos engineer points his torchlight at Papa's arm, hisses of exclamation flare up from my people. Even I cannot hold the "heii" that escapes my lips.

"What is this?" Papa shoves his hand at John. "This is not palm oil." Papa's hand is covered in viscous, black and slightly brown liquid. It clings to his arm like thick tar. Evil, that is the word that comes to mind, it looks evil. Like it is alive and ready to consume anything in its path.

John swallows from the bottle in his hands, he gestures to the Lagos engineer. "Explain to these illiterate people just what exactly crude oil is." He staggers back to his boat-house, leaving my people to stare at the oil on Papa's arm as if it will attack them if they dare turn away.

The SHELL DARCY people fully start drilling oil the next day. My people are barred from going close to the forest area, o⊡r fishing limited to the shallow waters near the riverbank—just for now, the Lagos engineer explains.

Bassey and Dooh go to sell their catch. I do not have the mind to fish today so I stay at home. From the village, I hear the falling of more trees and the ruckus from yesterday continues. No matter how hard I try, my textbooks cannot distract me.

Unable to sit still, I wear my d⊡nlop slippers and go to the riverbank. The boat-houses are empty save for one; it is William who occupies it, I ignore his greeting and he makes no further attempt to talk to me.

The sight here causes my chest to ache. It is much worse seeing the destruction than hearing it: the screeching of the birds as they fly away to seek shelter elsewhere, the cries of the trees as they fall, the teeth-jarring noise of the drills as they break into the ground.

"This people will destroy our village now," I cry.

"I'm sorry," I hear William say behind me. I did not hear him approach. "This is just the beginning, this destruction, I've seen them do it in the other countries. I hate this!" he spits with venom.

His words anger me even more, his privileged words; I am angry that he has the privilege to say he hates something that does not affect him. "Wetin be that?!" I exclaim, forgetting my proper

English. It feels like a sham now, to speak the words from the books of the white men.

The thing I ask about is a black oily mass floating across the edge of the riverbank. I scoop the thing out of the water, part of it comes away but more remains in the water, floating away from me. The oil clings to my hand, squeamish and tar-like in a kaleidoscope of colour. Why do the white men call it black gold when the oil is a mural of paint, splashed with red, orange, yellow, and blue.

The oil, it is a rainbow.

"This is just the beginning," William mutters as he uses his starchy brown shirt to clean off the oil from my hand. It doesn't clean off completely, I don't think it can, don't think it ever will.

PART 4

William was right. That was just the beginning. Oil is a curse.

In just two months that the Shell workers have been here, they have cleared out almost half of the forest. Before, you could not see the other side of the land because of the thick mangrove vegetation, most of it is gone now and what remains is coated in bitumen.

Worst of all, the workers are careless and nonchalant. They have started to bring in pipes that would be used to transport the oil to the refineries in the big city. Sometimes the pipes will roll off their trucks and onto our farms, flattening crops; one time, it fell on top of an elder's home. Almost crushing the poor man to death.

The white men and Shell workers have moved their boathouses to the other side of the river, closer to the forest and farther from us. They live in blatant splendour, a vast contrast to our village.

As if that is not enough, they treat us like animals. Shoving us when we're in their way, harassing our women and taking food from us without paying. The villagers grow angrier as days go by, they do not say it out loud but I know they blame Papa, they think he connived with the white men to sell the village and is secretly eating the money alone.

If blame falls on Papa, then ultimately, it falls on me.

I dodge an errant Shell worker on my way to the riverbank.

"Idiot," he mutters. I pause but continue on my way: Bassey and Dooh would be waiting for me already. Today is Bassey's birthday, we have decided to fish for only half the morning then celebrate in the big city when we go to sell. A little bit of happiness blossoms in my chest, it has been long since I felt this way.

"Oyoyoooo, big men," I shout in greeting, ready to resume the day with jesting and play fights. Bassey and Dooh do not respond. They are staring at the water as if they have seen a ghost. They and the other fishermen. My heart falters a bit, what is it again?

When I get closer, Dooh points at the water to show me what they are staring at although there is no need for him to: bloated dead fish float belly □p, h□ndreds of them. More white bellies pop up father down the river, so maybe more than hundreds. The bodies are tainted black with oil; it is an obscene image. Dead fish floating in rainbow patches.

Bassey claps and folds both his arms across his chest with a h□ff. "Ah Mene, see wetin these people don do o, see wetin them dey do us Mene."

I reach into the water and p□ll o□t the dead fish closest to me. It is slimy and cold. I throw the fish on the sand and bring o□t another one. The fishermen follow my c□e, taking o□t dead fish one after the other until the area is clear. Then we get our nets and untie the boats and row into the river. Not a word is uttered.

Dooh is the first to throw his net today, his mother's sickness has worsened and the herbs he bo□ght no longer take effect. "Nothing dey this water," Dooh says sadly as he tells us to bring up the net. As usual, he is correct. The net comes out empty, but heavy with the dark oil that clings to it.

The other fishermen gape at Dooh's net. Never! Never in o□r lives have we seen a net empty after it goes into the water. A headache blooms in my head as we row back to the riverbank. There, we b□rn the dead fish we had gathered.

"This night, I am coming back here," I say to them, "and I will row to that place and destroy whatever I see."

When I come back under the dark cloak of the night, I meet all of them there, in addition to some of the farmers and younger boys. We row as quietly but as fast as we can to the forest area. We leave o□r boats a little bit far off the shore and swim the rest of the way.

The lights in the boat ho□ses are off, b□t still, we lighten o□r footsteps. I am surprised to see that there are no soldiers, I expected to meet some resistance. It seems the Shell workers grew complacent since our village showed no signs of rebellion before.

We are met with trucks and barrels upon barrels of oil. The pipe closest to the water is broken and oil gushes out of it like a geyser and pours unrestrained into the river. It is an absolute mess. We don't waste time; Bassey, Dooh and some other boys tinker with the trucks—cutting wires and stabbing tires with sharp nails. I lead the rest; they want to destroy the pipelines but that would be shooting ourselves in the foot.

This resistance, though small and perhaps practically unreasonable, leaves us feeling triumphant as we head back to the village. I know that we will no longer sit and watch as they abuse our land and poll□te it in their selfish q□est for oil money.

A soft, hoarse voice wakes me. "Mene, Mene, stand up, you have to run." It is followed by a heavy slap to my face and that is enough to send away the sleep I sorely crave.

"What is it?" I crack my eye open to see the pale white skin of William. William? What is he doing back in Ogoni? He had left with Sunday's wife a week after the white men showed us their black gold.

"You need to run Mene, my father is coming with soldiers, they will arrest all of you," William coughs out as he pushes me out of my bed and hands me my dunlop slippers. "I heard of what your people did, you shouldn't have done that."

"Eh William hold it! You don't get to tell us what we can and cannot do."

William shakes his head and drags me out of my house. "Shit," he mutters into the gun barrel pointed at our heads. It's too late, the soldiers are already here. They bang on doors and drag out any boy they see, even those that weren't part of our little sabotage team.

They round us up, pushing William to the side, where John grabs a handful of his shirt then hits him. William staggers to the gro□nd, then gets □p and sq□ares his sho□lders in defiance. John hits him again and this time, he does not get up. His father signals one of the soldiers to take him. Our eyes meet as his limp form is dragged away, and I know I will never forget William—I know I will never see him again.

Papa limps out of the house—he is still recovering from a farming incident with a hoe—his ire is directed at John. "Have you not done enough to this village? You deceive us, spoil our means of livelihood and do not give us the money you promised. I say is it not enough *Oga* John."

John sneers at him, "Go to your corrupt government and ask for your money." He instructs the soldiers to bundle us into their trucks.

The entire village is silent, in shock. How did we go from a tiny prosperous village to this? I see this question in their eyes.

Deki runs at the soldier that has Bassey. "Don't take brother Bassey, please leave my brother alone!" Her cries are c□t off as the soldier pushes her away. That is when all hell breaks loose. Bassey struggles free from the hold of the soldier restraining him and punches him. Fueled by his actions, the other boys begin to jump o□t of the tr□cks and fight back. I join them.

A gunshot is followed by a scream, a body thuds to the ground. Another scream, "Dafe!" The boy on the ground is Bassey's brother, his immediate younger one. I don't need to check to know that he is gone.

The hushed silence is broken by Bassey's sorrow. "Why you shoot am! Wetin the boy do you wey you shoot am!" Bassey cries out in a guttural cacophonous voice that does not belong to him and goes for the soldier with the raised gun. The soldier easily restrains Bassey and hits him with the butt of the gun. Bassey crumples to the ground.

I blink, how did we get here? How?

"Enough." Papa limps to John and leans into him, close enough for their noses to touch. "I am the chief of this village, this boys act only under my command. Leave them and take me."

John and the white men leave □s in clo□ds of d□st flared □p by their trucks. Blood seeps into the earth where Bassey's brother lies unmoving. Deki lies on top of him, her body heaving with heavy sobs; her remaining siblings carry her away. They go into their house and do not come out again.

We bury Dafe after Bassey rouses. Just the three of us and the rest of his siblings. Dooh sings that song, the one about the boy who has to prove himself as a warrior by fighting an invincible monster.

At first, I think the song is inappropriate—the white man John and the soldiers are not invincible—but when it's time for us to cover up the shallow, hastily dug grave, I realize it is, because John and the soldiers aren't the monsters, SHELL DARCY is.

"Wetin we go do about your Papa?" Bassey asks me after he throws the last piece of sand on his brother's grave. Dooh and I exchange looks.

"Why don't yo□ go home with yo□r siblings first, console them, then we will—"

"Mene no dey speak all this English for me." Bassey swivels around. "Them don take my brother, you go allow them carry your Papa join?"

That's when I understand that Bassey somehow wants to get his brother back through my father. I wish desperately that he will choose another way to express his grief. I am not that lucky; I see the look in his eyes, Bassey wants revenge.

"Tomorrow," I assure him, "we will go and protest in the big city." Bassey nods but I can see that a protest is not what he wants.

We leave in the morning; the only people left behind in the village are elders too old to manage the trek and children too young to be exposed to the cruelty we might encounter.

The big city introd□ces itself to □s with Shell refineries where thick black plumes of smoke curl out of tall cylindrical cement buildings.

Our protest is a silent one. I do not want the government to have another excuse to pack all of us like sardines to jail. We carry placards with daring words mixed with curses.

Shell is killing us and killing our land
Leave our village alone

Glass flaring kills Ogonis
Assassins, go home
Shell is hell. This one is mine.

A group of soldiers approach us, I turn back to find Bassey to hold him from doing anything rash, but Bassey is not amongst us. Dooh notices this too and shrugs at me. I tell my people to relax while I have a few words with the soldiers.

They laugh at us after I explain why we are here, then they let us continue our protest. I see why much later when our protests are met with silence. Occasionally, cars drive by and bathe us with mud water. No government official comes to address us like I had expected.

We are nothing to this people. This affluent people in the city who live in houses of brick and mortar while we live in sheds. Their wealth is an affront to us, it protests for them so they don't have to.

This becomes our routine for the next few months, wake up, go to the city, protest, be ignored. We do it over and over again until our voices become weak and scratchy and tired. The number that follows me dwindles every day but I go regardless until one day it is just me and Dooh, with Bassey who disappears like he always does.

Papa is never returned to us, to me. I know the villagers think good riddance to bad rubbish. He is the one who agreed to the lies of the white men. They do not remember how they danced and posed for John's camera. But I point no fingers. No one is to blame except Shell Darcy and the conniving white men and a government who sold us out to Shell.

One day, when I stop at a bar to buy *pure* water, I see on the news that our village is not the only one that Shell has destroyed and we are not the only ones protesting, however, some communities use a different form of protest, they are not as peaceful as we are. In place of placards, they carry guns.

Word spreads like wildfire about this people who choose to fight back, even our small peaceful protest is added into the mix, the government is quick to label us *Niger delta militants.*

Militants: the word leaves a bad taste in my mouth. We are so much more than that, we are people who were cheated and stolen from. People who simply want their land and source of livelihood back, but the thing is, when the world gives you a label, it is impossible to shed. They say that is what you are, so you must become.

That is how we become the *Niger delta militants,* and from there, we become a national threat.

PART 5

There is a structure.

Its design is rudimentary, consisting of old corroded pipes and drums welded together. Within the drums, oil boils and releases fumes that sting my eye. On the oil cloaked ground just beside the drums is a gun.

Someone is speaking to me, but the words fade in and out, I put my finger in my ear and twist it three times to make sure my hearing is still alright. It is, but there's a slight ringing.

"E make sense abi or wetin you feel?"

Bassey, he's the one talking to me. I look at him with my brows furrowed in the middle. "What do I feel about this?" An illegal oil refinery. He's asking what I feel about an illegal refinery. "You want to know what I have to say about you committing a crime?"

Bassey kisses his teeth and shoves my shoulder, not hard but with enough force for me to know I've angered him. He goes to one of the two oil drums and connects another pipe to it.

"Dooh," he calls out to Dooh who stands mute beside me, "come make I show you this thing." Dooh doesn't move. I can see the gears in his mind, whirring and clicking, trying to reconcile the Bassey who holds a gun with the Bassey we knew.

When and how did he even get the money to build this. Then I remember that each time we went to the big city, Bassey disappeared, and when we came back, he wouldn't be in the village. I'd been so caught up in my protest that I hadn't taken the time to process everything.

"The money, who gave it to you?" First things first.

He stops tinkering with the barrel for a second to look at me, deciding if he should answer. "E get one politician."

I raise my brows urging him to continue. Bassey groans and drops the rubber pipe in his hands. He coughs and cleans his blackened hands on his shorts. "That day wey we start protest, e get one politician wey call me. He talk say he know wetin dem do my brother and your Papa."

Out of the corner of my eye, I see Dooh peer into the oil drum. He does it again, distracting me. "After that?" I say, returning my attention to Bassey.

He shrugs. "Eh him say he go give me money to do this thing, and we go share the money half half." Bassey presses his mouth into a thin line as his shoulders go rigid, he goes back to working the pipes. He's dismissed me.

"Bassey, I know you're grieving and that's why you made this decision but ah, e no good." I point to the other side of the river. "See now, what will happen when they reach here?" I ask, referring to the Shell Darcy people.

"We go move."

"We? You want us to put our lives in danger to make money for a politician who probably had a hand in what happened to us in the first place? Think now Bassey! I'm not doing this with you o."

Bassey pauses, the air between us goes frigid, curling up in my nostrils and threatening to choke me. "Why?"

I lose my patience, this boy can't possibly be serious. "Are you crazy, this is illegal, if they catch you—no I don't even care about that. It's too dangerous, what if there's a fire!"

"That one no concern me. If you no want do—dey go. After all na your Papa cause all this thing wey dey happen."

My heart lurches. There it is, the unspoken words no one dared to say to me, out here in the open. I should have known it was Bassey who would dare to tread where no one else would. Dooh flinches at his words but does not say anything, like I expect him to, but it's fine—Dooh is a peacemaker.

"If I remember well Bassey, you were among the people who agreed with my father's decision."

"So? Na still your idiot Papa cause am." He comes up to me and draws up to his full height, daring me to say a word.

The feeling in my chest is inexplicable, I've never felt this way before so I can't quite put my fingers on it. I want to say this is rage but I'm not sure, but what I do know is that it has a touch of sorrow to it.

Our fight is like a flurry of choreographed moves, like the steps have been set up for Bassey to win, although I throw the first punch. With blow after blow, he releases all of the pent up anger in him. At some point, Bassey begins to cry and I do nothing but let him use me as an emotional crutch. When he is done, he tosses me aside like a rag.

"Mene I—" he begins to say, but I cut him off, I can't bear that slight apology I see in his eyes while his fists say otherwise.

"No be your fault Bassey, no be your fault at all." It is as if he has beaten all my proper English out of me, the thought almost makes me laugh. "Dooh make we leave this fool, he will find what he is looking for very soon."

Dooh does not follow, he stands beside Bassey, declaring silently whose side he has chosen. "My Mama dey sick Mene, we need money for medicine."

I blink and shake my head, making a flash of pain dance in my eyes. "Okay, okay o, good-luck to both of you." That is the last thing I say to them even though I want to say more.

We don't see each other much after that, I keep to my house when I'm not protesting as a one-man squad in the city. It's difficult but we manage to do it—avoid each other that is. I wish I could hate them.

Instead, I read the bible I found in my Papa's empty room, then I pray every day to a God I do not believe in. I beg him to send us back in time, back to before when John and Sunday came. I tell him that if he does, I will take a rifle and shoot both of them without hesitation. "I no be killer o God but I go do am." I have turned to pidgin, let the white men have their language!

If there is one thing I'll never let the oil take from me, it's my river. It does not matter that the oily mass clings to my skin each time I get in, it does not matter if there are no more fish, this river—it's still mine. So I trade my nets for buckets, the fish for sand, and become a sand fisherman.

It is just me and five other men. The rest of the fishermen and farmers have joined Bassey. I don't blame them either, especially our farmers; it must have been painful to watch the oil seep into the soil and eat their crops. To see their livelihood stolen in the blink of an eye. All their hoeing and tilling overtaken by marshy black oil.

Over the next months, I fall into a routine. I get up as early as I can and head to the riverbank. There I strip and enter the water, naked as the day I was born. I use a bucket to swim to the bottom of the river, gather sand with it, then swim up and empty the sand in my boat. It's delicate work but not hard to get used to.

Then I sell the sand to the cement factory in the big city, luckily I don't have to find how to lug the sand all the way there, the factory sends a truck every day, I and the other sand fishers fill it up and get paid. The money is not much but it keeps our bellies full.

After this, I jog back home, change my clothes and carry the *Shell is hell* placard. I protest every day while my people remain in the village sick and dying from the pollution. Still, my father is not returned to me.

The sun is cruel today, its rays nip at the back of my neck, threatening to melt my skin off.

I try to work faster but the hard labour is beginning to take its toll on me, my limbs feel loose and separate from my body, the swelling of my legs should feel heavy but it does not—not to mention how deep my eyes have sunken into my head, red and swollen and contrasting with blue-tinged lips.

"Mene e don do, no kill yourself." Inengite, another sand fisher, calls out to me as he pushes his boat past. Both of us have established something of a partnership, similar to what I had with Bassey and Dooh but never the same. God I miss them! They do not come to the village anymore, sleeping and eating in that illegal refinery like their very lives depends on it.

"Mene I say your sand don dey OK!" Inengite warns again, but I tell him to go ahead, I need to work this exhaustion out of my body. *Poor boy,* he says as he leaves, and I am reminded that today is the day I turn sixteen. I am now a full man, as my people would say. I feel older than that *sha*.

Struggle: it has a way of ageing you beyond your years.

"One more," I say to myself, ignoring the heaviness in my hands, then I grab my bucket, but a sudden cough seizes me. My abdomen constricts painfully and I bend over to release the cough, what comes out is a chunky glob of blood. I stare at the blood as it melts into the river water and flows away, then I take my bucket and swim down.

It still managed to shock me a little—the blood. "Chronic bronchitis," the doctor in the big city had announced with a grimace on his pockmarked face. I had not bothered to ask him what it was, I knew instantly that sand money could not treat it.

Above the water, a boat flies past, followed by another. This one goes so fast it causes ripples in the water; my boat overturns, pouring all the sand on me and back into the river. The sand sinks, pushing me down, taking hours of labour along with it. I bite my lips and continue to swim up, willing the tears that form in my eye to go away.

As I swim up, something catches my eye through the murky water, I see it clearly because it gleams in the sun. A gun. I swim under my boat, using it as cover. I've had too many traumatizing moments with guns to let these men catch me even though I don't know what they are here for.

I watch from the cover of my boat, three boats with the Shell Darcy logo, each with at least five army men loaded with g□ns and bullets strapped around their shoulders. They are headed in one direction; my mouth says it before even my brain can come around: "Bassey, Dooh!"

My following actions are like an out of body experience, somehow I find myself swimming across the river with long b□t slow strokes. The soldiers are long gone now, and only the slap of my heavy strokes dist□rbs the river. I make it to the illegal refinery coughing and hacking.

Hot pressure builds in my chest but I ignore it as I pull myself out of the river.

If ever I needed an accurate image of chaos, this would be it. The men from my village take unpracticed aim at the soldiers, lucky if a bullet hits, unlucky if it doesn't. I see one of them go down, I recognize him. His wife gave birth to his sixth child just yesterday.

Another man takes a bullet to the head, his body hits the ground, his mouth open in a silent scream. Through all this, I do not spot Bassey and Dooh from where I stay hidden. The pressure in my chest spreads.

I force myself to think over the deafening sound of gunshots and war. Dooh is smart, Dooh wouldn't let Bassey stay behind to fight no matter what. My eye drifts to the other end of the refinery, the part that serves as a shortcut back to our village.

Again, my body moves before my mind is ready, I am half running, half crawling through the bushes hoping I do not get spotted by a soldier. My prayer is short-lived, because just as I utter it, a soldier slams into me, tackling me headfirst to the ground. He flips me over and pushes my head into a deep puddle of oily water; I make the mistake of inhaling as I struggle. My lungs and nostrils are filled within seconds, my chest burns.

The soldier raises my head up; I don't have enough time to gasp before he pushes it back down, this time into the earth, and I swallow a handful of mud. If I wasn't being suffocated to death, I would be irritated by the earthworm I also swallowed.

Darkness flashes across my eyes, briefly, but I understand what it means and I make my peace with it. I always thought I would die with a lot of regrets; wishing I had found a way to leave our village, a way to bring my Papa back, a way to turn back time to before everything. But none of that crosses my mind. Instead I think about Bassey and Dooh and how I would die a thousand times over for them.

Then I hear someone shout my name, and the soldier is no longer pressing my head into the mud.

"Hold his other hand, fast!" That's Dooh, I recognize his voice even though he sounds different. Older and tired.

They wipe the mud from my eyes, it stings but my vision returns immediately. "Let's go." Dooh hoists my arm over his neck and pulls me along.

"Mene, wetin you come find here," Bassey says, out of breath.

I suddenly feel the urge to laugh, what else does he think I came to find? "Don't be stupid Bassey," I reply and sling my arm off his neck. We begin to run faster.

It is getting darker, so we have to squint to see where we are going, which is why we don't see the soldier or the yawning mouth of his gun until it's too late. "Bassey!" Dooh moves to push Bassey away from the line of the bullet, I get there before him and shove Bassey, we both fall to the ground with a grunt.

Something lodges itself in my chest, it feels like an errant pebble has been chucked at me. A burning, aggravating sensation grows in my chest. Another bullet fires; Dooh has killed the soldier. My Dooh killed a soldier.

When I roll off Bassey, blood covers his shirt, staining it red.

The feeling in my chest tells me the blood is mine not his. The realization hits him and Dooh at the same time, just when I collapse to the ground and black out.

I come to and the first thing I see is Bassey cro□ched over me with tears and snot rolling down his face. I turn his head a little to see that we are in a small cave and it is completely dark outside.

"Mene why you come that place, why Mene ah." He grips both sides of his head and drags at his hair.

I make a frail attempt to hit him. "You be my brother for life; both of you, abi you no remember." And I mean it. "Bassey no be your fault. I don dey go small small since before now," just then my throat fills with liq□id and I co□gh it □p; it is red and thick as if to punctuate my words.

Bassey is a mess, a crying snivelling mess, I expected him to be braver than this. "Mene abeg I tey god beg you, stand up."

"Yo□ go promise me something first."

"Eh?"

"You go commot this village after today, carry Deki and your siblings leave this place." I turn slightly, "Dooh you too. This oil na curse, leave am!"

Dooh scoots closer to me and puts his hand on my forehead, then he closes my eyes because Dooh always knows. He begins to whisper our song, the one about the warrior boy. Bassey joins him.

"Of sticks and stones he was not made
yet the boy remained brave
against the monster; invisible it was
how would he prevail against the unknown
the boy cries as claws of steel rake through his heart
See how the boy bleeds
proclaimed a warrior
but only by his death"

I sing it with them, my voice fading in and out.

Once I read a book that was not given to me by my Papa, it was about death. There was a part that stuck, the words imprinted in my memory like ink on paper. It said, w*hen a person dies, his soul carries on the memory of how he died.*

I imagine it is true as I sing the last line of our song. That my soul will come out to carry the memory of how I died, that my soul will never forget the image of me ravished by life and covered in black gold, my feet tinged with a kaleidoscope of colors where the oil has mixed with water.

Yes, my soul will hold the memory of me leaving this world in a baptism of blood and oil.

Iloz⊡mba Otitoch⊡kw⊡ Amanda is a messenger for fictional characters and often refers to herself as three owls disguised as a human.

She is obsessed with African mythology and wants to write a speculative fiction novelette inspired by African gods, that is, if she can manage to put down her phone for more than a minute.

Ilozumba writes to tell the African story through the African lens.

Pollution's Makeup

Charlotte Kim

Ozone-freckled smog
lines an ash kohl waterline—
smoky city eyes.

Charlotte Kim is a writer based in Los Angeles. She recently graduated from the University of Southern California with a BA in Communication. Her work has been published in *The Parliament Literary Journal*, *Fifty Word Stories*, *Five Minutes*, *101 Words Flash Fiction*, and more.

The Watcher On the Wall

Rebecca Bratten Weiss

L□red by the first snow of winter,
my dead father managed to struggle out
of his grave on the far hill, managed to stagger
down into the walnut grove to meet me
as the heavy flakes fell.

He did not look bad. There
was a grandeur in his features in the half-light of
my torch.

What is it the snow does for the soil, again?
he asked me. Fixes nitrogen, I answered. No, wait
that's lightning. I couldn't remember what the snow
does except for cover the soil, cover us, cover the
living and the dead.

My father looked at me with some pity.
I saw then how his flesh had fallen away, how
his farm clothes were tattered.

I still know more than you do, girl, he said.
I am the watcher on the wall.

Before he died he'd said that,
called himself the watcher on the wall,
and it had meant only
that he watched men in bad suits on TV,
and read prophecies about the world's end.
It had been an old man's fantasy,
his final dodging of the tr□th.

Now I saw that he had found his wall.
His eyes were visionary, at last. Whatever it is
that's coming for us, he'd seen it.

He opened his mouth to tell and I saw the blue
of bones and

the snow came between us and our voices
were silenced, and he could give no warning.

Rebecca Bratten Weiss is a journalist, editor, and freelance academic residing in rural Ohio. Her creative work has appeared in a variety of publications, including *Two Hawks Quarterly*, *Presence*, *Connecticut River Review*, *Shooter*, *New Ohio Review*, *Gyroscope Review*, *The Seventh Wave*, and *Westerly*. Her collaborative chapbook *Mud Woman*, with Joanna Penn Cooper, was published in 2018, and her collection *Talking to Snakes* by Ethel Zine and Micro Press in 2020. She is a two time Pushcart nominee, and winner of the Helen Schaible Memorial Sonnet Contest, Modern category.

A brief history of misery

Amirah Al Wassif

Among the stones, there was a flower that reached o⊡t to me.
Many years ago, I dreamt of the Arabian Nights
When I woke up I found myself laughing
Nothing wrong with the laughter
But we shouldn't take history seriously when it turned into a big joke.
I sat at the edge of the battle
Dressed like a warrior
I am not a half person anymore
No Matter how my society categorizes me
No Matter how the world introduces me
I stand in a proud position
Pouring my excitement into the Revolution's womb
I run with all my might seeking a door or a window
I found nothing
I type on my Google page
'Freedom'
I searched many times
But found no results.
I recalled the rooster's sound in our tales
I waited for its appointment
But nothing came.
I shouted like a child
Who had her first sight of a gorilla
I moaned
All the women who were hidden under my skin moaned louder.
We are not a family
We are one.
We are tied to each other against the walls of the prison.
It took a very long time to crawl from under the tunnels
Climbing the highest trees
Rubbing our faces with the world's maps
Among the stones, there was a flower that reached o⊡t to me.
I was born with a great motivation to scratch the sky

No Matter how many people limited my power
No Matter how hard the world fought me.

Amirah Al Wassif has two poetry collections: *For Those Who Don't Know Chocolate* [Poetic Justice Books & Arts, February 2019] and the illustrated children's book, *The Cocoa Boy and Other Stories* [Poetic Justice Books & Arts, February 2020]. Her poems have appeared in print and online publications including *South Florida Poetry*, *Birmingham Arts Journal*, *Hawaii Review*, *The Meniscus*, *Chiron Review*, *The Hunger*, *Writers Resist*, *Right Now*, and several other publications, and her upcoming poetry collection (*How to Bury a Curious Girl*) will be published in April 2022 by Bedazzled Ink P□blishing LLC, Fairfield, CA.

Sweetwater, Poison: from the Cape Fear River to the Bay of Fundy

Brianna Cunliffe

Last September, they told us not to drink the water.

Our water, from our river, the same water that's cooled every summer thirst, washed every dish at every birthday party, rinsed the sap off every Christmas since the day I was born.

The advisory was only a precaution, the news broadcast reassured us, but the Food Lion and Harris Teeter shelves were empty in hours flat. Even the Smartwater, the Fiji, the fancy-pants expensive stuff no North Carolinian in their right mind would ever buy in bulk—every case was gone.

Up the river in Fayetteville, the DuPont team responsible for the release of the chemical driving the drinking ban was gathered in some PR war room, but downstream, we turned to sweet tea, lemonade, coffee, orange juice, every other thing in the fridge, always starting for the tap and remembering just as we began to turn it.

But of course, some people went right on drinking the water, just like some people have parties on the beach during Category 4 storms, because this is the Carolina coast and we are nothing if not accustomed to disaster.

This was before Florence, when we had enough distance from a truly bad storm to cheer on the fledgling squalls spiraling off the Gulf Coast, craving the respite from life and school they would bring. And if they ever threatened with any seriousness to arrive, it was a crude, manic, festive vacation, as we boarded up windows, spray-painting challenges or prayers on plywood, surfers racing for storm swell as the ocean churned and they howled the joy of getting waves as close to California big as our east coast shore could ever muster.

In Wilmington, North Carolina, our history is made up of pirates, hiding behind piny shoals from the law, of stubborn generals in the last bastion of the civil war, flowering azalea, cobblestones, steeples on every corner, college basketball and hurricane parties, and so some people flapped their hands, scoffed at science, and went right on drinking the water.

In the coming months, clumsy local-news reporting fed us the piece-meal story: Once upon a time, DuPont, nee Chemours, manufactured shiny new Teflon upstream in Fayetteville, and to make it extra-shiny, they used a chemical (and I swear this is the name, though I know it sounds like a comic book kryptonite) called GenX. It flowed with the rest of the sludge deemed safe into the Cape Fear River. And one day, in a series of routine tests, they found it in the drinking water. Someone saw the results and rang the alarm bells, even if they didn't know what they were ringing them for.

The impacts of GenX on human health are unclear. It's a new chemical, one of many PFAs beginning to be called "forever chemicals", developed as a replacement for the blacklisted PBDEs of the 1980s. They exist in a kind of grey regulatory limbo, not yet classified as toxic or completely cleared. They've caused cancer in some lab rats—news that makes your stomach turn when you turn on your tap—but it hasn't been enough for companies to forgo their profitable use.

What was clear, though, was that the bottled Fiji water my more nervous neighbors were using to brush their teeth with wasn't going to do any good. GenX had been in our water for almost a decade already, at 130,000 parts per trillion. If it was going to hurt us, the damage was done.

So there was a great Southern shrug, and we all turned on our taps. Just like turning up the music at a hurricane party as the winds howl. What's done is done, what'll come will come.

Meanwhile, every agency with an acronym east of Raleigh was floundering. The bogeyman of this long-term mystery molecule was proving impossible to wrangle, harder even than the coal ash spill from a few years back in the same long-suffering river. Suddenly its presence in the water and its questionable past were splayed out on scrolling cable news bulletins night after night. There were town halls packed full of scared angry people who wanted to know what was in their water, and the harried municipal inspector fresh out of school, the underpaid chemists from the treatment plant—they all had to tell their neighbors: *we don't know.*

Let me be very clear: Wilmington is not Flint, Michigan. Environmental disasters always disproportionately affect already marginalized communities, hitting hardest the people who can't afford a case of Fiji water or people in food deserts who walk to the corner store for groceries and couldn't carry five cases even if they could afford it. And parallels of negligence are certainly present. But GenX isn't lead. Our children aren't dying. And our elected officials were blindsided by its presence in our water, just like us, even if the Chemours executives were not.

This is the place I am from: where a river only this year after tireless fighting has stopped carrying a wild-card chemical downstream into the taps of everyone I know and love, where coal ash was spilled in the same waters a few years back and there was never just restitution, Where surrounding farmland is plagued by algae-choked lakes, animal refuse is dumped with abandon as factory farms go unregulated, where building codes allow brand sparkling new oceanfront construction for the revenue they will generate despite the constant sea level rise and erosion, where people stare stubbornly into the eyes of storms like Florence, which took seventeen lives and left my hometown an island, which worsen with every passing year.

This is the place I live now: where I sit in a classroom in Maine and listen as a professor talks about the sublime American wilderness, where I major in a field of study centered around the 'environment', in a town where farmer's markets dot the village green and grocery stores have started charging per plastic bag.

I write these words on a scientific station off the coast of Canada on a summer arts fellowship, with hundreds of miles of ocean between me and a factory, where we count with care the eggs of even the common gull and are careful not to let even hand soap contaminate the nesting sites of sparrows, where at night the only visible sign of human industry under the stars with the milky way caressing their swirling center is the lighthouses to the south and north. I am paid two dollars an hour more than the minimum wage in my state to write poetry about storm petrels and honeybees and the fog rolling in from the sea.

And at first glance, this makes sense to me. After all, there are places like Kent Island, and places like Wilmington. There and Here.

When most people talk about the environment, they mean Kent Island and the jungles of Belize, beautiful wondrous pristine places, distant places, There.

But beer cans in estuaries and a state park with trails layered over tore-up old motorbike paths, and the muddy river under fourth of J□ly fireworks flowing, and the creek behind the s□bdivision, and the GenX flowing downstream—the environment is hiding Here, too.

There is an incredible contempt in America for the middle landscape—a term environmental scholars use to describe places like Here. Not catastrophe and ruin, oil spills or garbage dumps or black-lung from coal or the radium-girl shocking headlines from old factories, but the Here—the backyard grass that needs mowing.

But the problems in our thinking are the hardest to shift, especially when the pull of the There is so deeply ingrained, and we are all forced to deal with the drudgery and carnage of the Here.

Like the officials in my home town with their alarmist call to t□rn off the taps or like the D□Pont inspectors who said nothing all those years, it is either feast or famine with the American imagination. We invoke a love of Nature to save the redwoods, while it isn't even a word we connect with planted petunias on overpasses or roots scrabbling up in vacant lots.

No one is paying me to write poems abo□t the flooded cobblestones on 3rd Street after the hurricane, greasy with sunscreen and gasoline, abo□t the retention pond my dad and I fished in, always catching turtles on accident; no one is paying me to write poems about the bare shelves of Food Lion, even the Fiji water gone.

But maybe the answer is that I will anyway. Because I am sitting in this pristine paradise with all the privilege that comes along with it, and I'm telling you: they're the same gulls circling overhead, the same goldenrod that grows along the highway in the place I am from. At home and far afield I have the same right to clean air and water and a livable planet, regardless of how well it translates into our romantic ideals of wilderness.

The "environment" is of no use to us if it ceases to exist where it cannot fit easily into poems like "Leaves of Grass" or even "The Wasteland". Feast or famine are not the ways to live in the world. The power of activism spurred by imagination is futile if our contempt for the middle landscape blinds us to the necessity of change.

We all live in landscapes that shapeshift, passing through blurring borders of Here and There. It can seem impossibly incongruent: the carelessness of a tossed-aside beer can on a commercial shore and the gentle fastening of a thousand-dollar tracker to the wing of a burrowing grey bird.

But I am learning to blur these lines, to unhitch my sense of beauty from an obligation to perfection. Like anyone with the privilege to experience such beauty, I must grapple with my longing to always live on Kent Island, to set these places on their pedestals. I know that my hometown's muddy river water is not truly separate from the waters crashing on this untouched shore. It is all flowing from the same headwaters; we all live downstream.

Brianna Cunliffe (she/her) is an environmental justice activist and writer currently studying at Bowdoin College. As a queer woman who grew up on a rising shoreline, her work is animated by fierce love of the fragile places we call home. In 2019, she served as the artist-in-residence on the Kent Island Scientific Station in the Bay of Fundy, generating poetry, short story, and essay focused on the climate crisis. Her poems and short stories have been published in *Storm Cellar*, *Claw and Blossom*, *Blind Corner*, *isacoustic** and more.

Apology for the Divine Masculine

Jacob Budenz

"And the ship, the black freighter,
disappears out to sea, and on it is me."

Wetlands become one with the rising gulf
as oil rigs drink the earth's secret juices
and phallic man-made things do other rapey things
to things to which we have ascribed yonic features
and so forth in a pastiche of sexes assigned
to things that never asked not to be sexless.

Does Mother Earth apologize when she
retaliates, swallowing swamp towns
and eating away at the foundations
of coastal cities, as my mother made
my sister and me apologize to our
abuser if ever we fought back?

If a drop of water fell
for each time I apologized for no reason
(besides that I grew up Baptist, believed
that God-on-Earth was tortured so God-up-There
would forgive me for being what He made me),
I'd sail across a sea of sorries,
beg mercy for reaching the shore,
and fall into the arms of the first
brute to excuse me for loving him.

Once, a middle-aged sorceress told me I'd never find love
unless I wrote an apology to the divine masculine for always
expecting the worst of him, and I told her, honey, not until he
writes me one for always proving me right. Once, a friend
told me that apologizing was my most feminine trait, as if
I weren't cooking dinner in heels and a backless dress, as if
femininity were skin I'd like to shed, and I said I apologized
for all men who wouldn't do the same, except, no, how
could I apologize for something I'd been assigned—
male, boy, man, him—but never really been?

If Mother Earth covers her face
in a veil of liquid blue shame
for what we've done to her
then I will not be sorry
it was her language,
not his, I learned.

Jacob Budenz is a queer writer, multi-disciplinary performer, educator, and witch with an MFA from University of New Orleans and a BA from Johns Hopkins University. The a□thor of *PASTEL WITCHERIES* (Seven Kitchens Press 2018), Budenz has work current or forthcoming in *Wussy Mag*, *Ghost City Review*, *Slipstream*, and *Entropy* as well as anthologies by Mason Jar Press and Unbo□nd Edition Press. You can follow Jake's work on Instagram (@dreambabyjake), Twitter (@jakebeearts), or the internet beyond (www.jakebeearts.com).

Photo credit Clare Welsh (@ClareWelsh on Instagram)

Nature's Chosen Pronouns

Miriam Navarro Prieto

**after Greta Gaard's* Toward a Queer Ecofeminism

But maybe nature isn't even
a "her".... *When nature is feminized*
and thereby erotized,
and culture is masculinized,*
the trouble starts, and it's the bad kind.
When the girl puts on a summer dress:
"she's asking for it".
When the soil is "too rich not to steal":
"she's asking for it".
When the non-westernized have (better)
non-reproductive sex and more
than two genders:
"they're asking for it".

So stop

the farther occ□pation of flesh,
of bodies made of earth.
Cut the virile organ
of colonization
before it brings more death
and the death of desire:
compulsory heterosexuality,
the age of the missionary,
*with the conqueror "on top."**

Miriam Navarro Prieto (she/her), Spanish artist who drifted from performance art to drawing, currently mainly focused on writing poems on a⊡tobiography, ecology, gender, q⊡eerness.... Her first self-published poem collection *Todo está vivo* is also available in English as *Everything Is Alive*, translated by the author. Her poems in English have been featured in journals like *Capsule Stories* and *The Pinch*, and her illustrations in *The Winnow*. She sends out a monthly bilingual newsletter-podcast on her creative process, with plants trivia and translated literature: tinyletter.com/miriam-navarro-prieto

Rooted

Wen-yi Lee

The mangroves inhale her, a buzzing, air-thick, knotted world. She has seen eighty-one years of their change—

Eighty-two? Perhaps eighty. The decades, like the roots, tangle themselves together, extend into murky depths. In her best sturdy shoes, Sik pads as quickly as she can over the silt. Her soles squelch in the softened edges. Brackish water laps at her feet, languid but somehow alive, thrumming with far-out currents. She thinks she catches the glint of crocodile eyes, but it sinks beneath the surface before she can be sure. Around the mud-flats, mottled brown crabs cling to the trees, make her mouth water with the pickled-vinegar memory, the porridge dinners. But no time for hearty meals now. She scuttles along.

The insects whine in a pulse; Sik absorbs it and her own blood hums in response. The paper flutter of wings, somewhere in the speckled canopy. She catches its tailstream the way her mother once taught her; her soul soars for a heightened breath and a flash of vivid, blurring colour before ripping away. She doubles over, groaning. Suddenly she is sweating more than she already was. That is a muscle she has not stretched in many years. Why, when there are now cameras and film and radios to bring the sights and sounds to you? She imagines what her mother would say: Careless. Arrogant. Rootless. *Jam bhoi sang tao lai.* You can't have it both ways.

Still, in that one soaring glimpse through the crow's eyes, she saw what she needed to see. They are coming.

She catches her breath and then picks up her pace, hobbling through the swamp. Her hospital gown snags on branches. The roots attempt to trip her; she drags one foot and then another over. Those muscles are also not what they once were. But she will not need them for much longer. Kuh, kuh, kuh. The bird coughs out its own song, but Sik hears familiar Teochew syllables. *Go, go, go.*

She goes, goes, goes. There was a time the mangrove forest grew every year, but there are few saplings now that the islanders have set their sights on more romantic plants to populate the land. All these trees are as old as she is. Older. As comforting as that is, it makes her ache. Not many choose to come here any longer. What will happen when they are outgrown?

Her foot catches on a jut of rock and she falls. Her knees nearly crumple with the impact and she hisses under her breath. Even now worrying about the future, she scolds herself, dusting off the sand and pushing herself to her feet.

The fall and the thoughts have cost her a precious minute, however. A hum of an approaching disturbance vibrates through the roots, sending the water shivering. Loud, clumsy, but too-fast footsteps, faster than she is. As she hobbles deeper into the swamp the trees seem to lean in—embracing, shielding, capturing, their earthy, slightly saline scent turning the air viscous. She does not know what she is looking for, exactly, but she will know it when she sees it. Hurry, hurry. An owl hoots low overhead. A flutter of white feathers. The shape of a woman sailing into the corner of her eye. Sik whips around, but it's only her own shadow racing over the water's surface. Her heart pounds nonetheless.

Then she looks across the bank and sees it. The spot at the edge of the water. The trees around it bow gently away, skirting the copse with their many legs to create a waiting little bay.

Hurriedly she finds the shallowest part of the water and splashes across. Some slithery brown creature jolts away from her in a panic. She scrabbles onto the opposite bank and drops onto the soil, panting. When she's collected herself, she lets the swamp sink back in, and she knows she's found the place.

The island has changed so rapidly her memories are stuttered instead of smooth. Suddenly, skyscrapers. Suddenly, condominiums. Suddenly, no more kampungs and only trishaws for tourists, and suddenly her children are speaking English and going to holidays in Japan every year, and suddenly, the city is unrecognisable. She does not always know if it still has a space for her, too old to learn the new ways, left behind in an island that no longer exists. But the mangroves have a place for her. This place, for her. It recognises her, the soil moulding soft around her limbs and the trees around her protecting.

She shuts her eyes briefly to the hum and chirping, the slosh of the slowed tides. She remembers times out in her father's fishing boat that the waves were not docile like this. They roared, black and spitting, threatening to upend the world. But the mangroves keep them safe from those waves; they tame them. She remembers a time when the mangroves wrapped the island. Now they cling in scraggly patches to the coast, replaced by factories and farms and slim pretty trees with concrete-stunted roots, and the dragon tides lick their lips at the land.

"Ma!"

Sik's eyes fly open. Bursting onto the opposite bank, tripping and cursing and sweating and wide-eyed, are her three children. She swears under her breath. She has to do it now.

She yanks off her shoes as her oldest son, Ah Seng, starts making his way across the shallows. He lunges forward, but she thrusts her feet into the water before he reaches her. The mud closes around her ankles.

"Go away, Ah Seng!" He's reached her now; she bats him away as he tries to pull her up. Her daughter and her youngest son, Ah Mui and Ah Yik, have started across as well, although Ah Yik's face twists as his expensive shoes touch the water.

"Ma," Ah Mui pleads from a distance. "Please come home. We already prepared the plot."

"I told you I don't want that plot right! I told you I wanted to come to the mangroves!" She finds the sudden strength to wrestle Ah Seng. A renewed energy has begun seeping into her veins, a new solidity firming up her muscles so badly ravaged by the illness. She sucks in a vicious breath. She has not felt this strong for many years. "You never listen to what I say, and you still dare be shocked."

"Who wants to come to the mangroves!" Ah Yik throws up his hands. He has abandoned his wading attempt and returned to dry land. His fancy shirt is soaked through, and it reminds her suddenly of him as a little boy wet from playing in the rain. She knows all his business partners call him Richard, but he will always be Ah Yik to her, the chubby child with his singlet turned translucent, wet hair dripping into his Milo. "You don't know what they're going to have to do to them in ten, twenty years—"

"In the park you have protection; we can look after you there," Ah Seng says, but his despairing expression, and the way he steps back from her, knows it is a lost battle. He can see the roots already twining up her legs.

Ah Mui is still trying. "We paid the shaman for a beautiful flower tree—"

"Flower tree! Flower tree do what? Let people pick only. Look nice nice in the park, hor? Let lightning strike only." Sik thumps her chest, which echoes like a drum. "My ah gong died in the war, you know! He fought against the Japanese. He never get to choose his path, but he die to protect the island, you think I want to be a flower tree! I old already, don't care about being beautiful. I don't need you to protect me." Ah Mui opens her mouth, but Sik cuts her off. "Need shaman somemore. Here, the old magic all connected, don't need anything but your spirit. Huh? You watch. You learn. Maybe when your time comes you will choose to be useful also, instead of become those trees that will blow over in a monsoon! Burden everyone only."

Her children exchange wary looks, one eye still on her as though surrounding a wounded animal. Sik sighs, even as she feels her spine straighten, her ribs begin knitting together. The magic has not yet reached her soft heart. "Come, lah," she says gently, reaching forward as much as her stiffened torso will allow. "Don't fight already."

After a fractured pause, Ah Mui is the first to stumble forward and fall awkwardly into her mother's browning arms. Sik kisses her forehead, the way she did when Mui was a girl. When Ah Mui pulls away her eyes are glistening and she sniffles.

Ah Seng gruffly holds her for one, three, five seconds, tucking his head in the crook of her neck. "Bye, Ma."

Ah Yik hesitates. Then, finally, he puts his feet in the water and trudges over to her. He brushes against her roots, but it doesn't hurt. His arms go around her, and by now she can't feel his chest rising and falling against hers, but she feels his chin shuddering against her shoulder. "Aiya," she croons, patting him stiffly on the back. Her hands are starting to harden, grow rough. "It's okay one, Ah Yik. The path not so hard. Can always come see Ah Ma."

When Ah Yik steps away, they are all three standing in front of her. Mui's arms are wrapped around her; Ah Yik has his hands shoved in his pockets. Ah Seng worries the hem of his shirt. Sik smiles at them as her fingers knot and lengthen, as her hair thickens and spreads, as her roots sink deeper and further into the swamp and the land. Her view of the children fades, and in its place rises a warm wind of greater consciousness. She sees the crocodile lazy on the water's edge; the hornbill that watches for prey; the spider weaving its web. She sees the island curving into the horizon. The boats that bob against the skyline; the buildings that perforate it. The bustling port and the floating market, the d□sting of trees along pin-straight roads.

Faintly, as she sinks into the swamp, she is aware of hands gently resting on her sides, cheeks against her branches, and three soft, steady pulses merging slowly into one. An old instinct swims hazily to the surface, melds into the new. I will protect you, she murmurs, and then she slips and twines and tilts her head upward, roots steadfast in the earth and arms reaching toward the sun.

Wen-yi Lee is from Singapore and likes writing about girls with bite, feral nature, and ghosts. Her work has appeared or is forthcoming in *Uncanny*, *Strange Horizons*, *Pseudopod* and *Anathema Magazine*, among others. She can be found on Twitter at @wenyilee_, and otherwise at wenyileewrites.com.

Footnotes from “Phosphates, Nitrates and the Lake A Incident: A Review.”

Mari Ness

1. Following the conventional naming system created by the Court of the Five Silver Moons.

2. Estimates derived from a survey of original documents and scholarly papers. The claim of 77,777 watermaidens by the Ambassador of the Court of the Indigo Sun, frequently cited by later scholars, may be safely dismissed as propaganda intended to convince Court members that this method of imprisonment was perfectly safe, as can the rumor that glimpses of multiple watermaidens are either an optical illusion or an enchantment cast by a single watermaiden to hide her precise location. The lake is not of sufficient size to support more than a few dozen watermaidens, and their skills in illusion and enchantment are limited. For more, see the comprehensive surveys by Thiten Amhranai on the history of watermaidens and their abilities and limitations.

3. Indeed, escapes from supposedly secure imprisonments appear to have been more common than actual secure imprisonments in ancient times. Even the most inaccessible, remote underworld areas were frequently breached by monsters and mortals.

4. Research conducted by mortals and others confirms that the limestone cave systems beneath the lakes are of fully natural origin.

5. As with their guards and jailors, the exact numbers are unknown, but at least 13 were confirmed to have been transported to the limestone caves, and possibly 64 more.

6. Cold iron, in addition to its other issues, would easily rust in the warm waters.

7. The slits in the grills were large enough to allow cave fish and other natural creatures to slide in and out of the caves, ensuring that they would suffer only limited effects.

8. This would not be a problem until centuries later, when mortals began searching the underwater caves with scuba gear. The

resulting scramble to enchant and hide the grills and divert curious mortals nearly drained two different Co□rts of their yearly s□pplies of liquid moonlight; see *The Fae Bulletin* for a detailed if somewhat sensationalistic report of the struggles to swiftly replenish those supplies.

9. Tho□gh notorio□sly fickle, watermaidens are capable of living underwater for extended periods of time, and thus have often been entrusted with equally perilous items.

10. The use of such fertilizers is common among mortals, who remain without access to other methods for encouraging plant growth.

11. Although increased algae growth had been observed in waters close to heavily fertilized areas, the effects of this growth were not well or widely understood by mortals or Court scholars at the time.

12. 19th century photographs taken by mortals show crystalline clear waters in the lake, along with ab□ndant fish, birds, and other wildlife. The lake bottom could easily be seen even in windy and cloudy conditions. Thanks to the freshwater spring, also tended by watermaidens, the lake remained at a near constant temperature year round, even in freezing conditions and in the peak of summer.

13. Ironically, the heavy use of phosphorus and nitrogen may have come about in part from an increased demand in many Courts at the time for mortal juices made from citrus fruits.

14. Phosphorus and nitrogen occur naturally in the mortal and nearby worlds, requiring no special enchantments for use. Because of this, they are often overlooked as potential hazards, and it is quite possible that the watermaidens never noticed.

15. The first reports of brown-tinged waters came from mortals in the 1940s, before any Court regularly reviewed mortal news or correspondence. Even now, many Courts decline to do so, citing concerns abo□t the effect of s□ch news on their denizens.

16. This may not have been the first attempt at comm□nication; the drops of water used by watermaidens to send messages are notoriously fragile. Attempts to update these communication systems have been sporadic and ineffective; even enchanted paper breaks down at their touch, and so-called waterproof electronics can only be used for brief periods.

17. It was not an illogical conclusion; although large die-offs of birds have often been associated with monstrous activity, they have been linked to mortals as well.

18. Supernatural involvement has been suspected, but not proven, in the 1980 dumping of DDE in the lake. It should be noted that mortals are perfectly capable of releasing pollutants on their own.

19. Scientific studies conducted by mortals cannot, of course, be entered into official Court records, but were and are still read and understood by Ambassadors and other Court interests. Many such studies can be found in Court libraries.

20. Photos taken by mortals in 1985 confirm that by this time, it was nearly impossible to see anything in the lake. Even large alligators could often only be spotted by the nearby movement of water.

21. By this time, the original white and grey sand at the bottom of the lake was completely covered in brown and black muck.

22. A search of mortal records suggests that the first deaths may have occurred in the late 1970s. A supernatural origin was not suspected until the mid-1990s.

23. The marks were not readily apparent on an initial inspection, but became visible under a mortal MRI machine, or when viewed through a moonlit-treated sapphire.

24. Although the enchantments could be enhanced to allow recipients to breathe for longer periods, such enhancements often left the recipients unable to move their arms for weeks or months afterwards. Understandably, most declined.

25. A later investigation ordered by the Queens of the Court of the Indigo Sun and the Court of the Five Silver Moons found neither the maps nor an explanation for their disappearance. Some have theorized that interests hostile to mortals, and unaware that the monsters imprisoned in the underwater cave systems also posed a threat to denizens of the Court, purposefully removed the maps to make it harder for anyone to find the gates—and thus notice their destruction.

26. At the same time, enchantments were hastily being replaced and replenished at the other cave systems, to strengthen the defenses against both escape and mortal detection.

27. The legal issue is somewhat murky. Watermaidens have never, of course, pledged allegiance to any specific court, and have

thus argued that they are not required to respond to any *fee decree* or Court summons, and may use their own judgement to manage any perceived or real threat, without consulting a Court. Interactions with mortals, however, typically fall under the regulation of the Courts, and these particular watermaidens, of course, had been charged with the guardianship of the lake and the monsters in the caves below by three separate Courts.

28. An Ambassador at the Court of the Seven Red Stars, argued that drastic measures—for example, restoring the lake to its earlier, crystalline state—could potentially cause more harm than it would mitigate, since even the most dull-witted mortal would question the rapidity of the change. Other officials at that Co⊡rt arg⊡ed that it was only fair for mortals, as the instigators of the pollution in the first place, to s⊡ffer the conseq⊡ences—even if some of those consequences were originally of supernatural origin.

29. This official co⊡nt is probably an ⊡ndercount. Other estimates suggest that over 7000 mortals and others died as a direct or indirect result of the predation, which may have occurred over a period of forty years.

30. As of this writing, muck continues to cover the bottom of the lake, and the waters remain brown and obscure. If the gates to the underwater caves have opened again, allowing the denizens there to depart, this cannot be determined from the surface. Birds and other wildlife, however, continue to return in greater numbers every year, and watermaidens have been spotted at the north of the lake, filtering some of the water thro⊡gh their transl⊡cent hands.

Mari Ness arguably spends too much time watching alligators swim across Lake Apopka. Her other work appears in *Tor.com*, *Clarkesworld*, *Lightspeed*, *Nightmare*, *Uncanny*, *Fireside*, *Nature's Futures*, *Diabolical Plots*, *Mermaids Monthly*, and *Strange Horizons*. Recent books include *Dancing in Silver Lands,* a tiny chapbook of tiny fairy tales; *Resistance and Transformation: On Fairy Tales,* an essay collection; and *Through Immortal Shadows Singing,* a poetry novella. For more, follow her on Twitter at @mari_ness, or visit her infrequently updated webpage at marikness.wordpress.com

Osprey's Sky

Takayuki Ino

White wave heads were making a line that stretched northward parallel to the coastline. A gentle sea breeze changed to an updraft on the sunshine-warmed land and pushed an osprey's wings up softly. The osprey rose higher and higher into the sky in wide circles. The bird felt the heat on its back. It was not uncomfortable. Its feathers held the warmed air, and it flapped its wings powerf□lly. The sky above the bird was endlessly blue, white tiny clouds slowly drifting in the wind.

The ocean below was rich and fertile. Cold and warm currents mingled, stirring and pulling up the minerals from the bottom. Large schools of small fish fed on the explosively growing plankton, and many seabirds had been attacking the schools.

On land, there was a deep forest. On the shore, there were harbors without ships and settlements without people. A brand new road ran straight ahead, and a high-voltage line was stretched beside it. Not a single car was visible. Beyond the road, something glistening and reflecting s□nlight looked like the water.

The flying osprey reached the glistening place. It flapped its wings once and then stopped moving. Suddenly it began to fall. It wasn't the sharp descent of a predator aimed at a fish, b□t the fall of an object trapped by gravity.

Away from its nest, which held two small eggs and its spouse, the osprey, swept by a slight change in wind direction, would never return.

Leaning my elbows on the dining room table, I looked out the window in a daze. The sun was setting, and the sky was orange. It must have been a lovely afternoon.

"What do you want me to do?" It was Mizuki, who had returned the food tray already. I didn't know if it was his breakfast or dinner. Eating at dusk always made me feel odd.

"Oh, please do it." I took off the integrating dosimeter aro□nd my neck and handed it to Mizuki.

Miz□ki was handy. He took off the panel on the back of the dosimeter with a small screwdriver and fiddled with a tiny switch. There was no one else in the cafeteria, so no one would see him.

"It's about time, don't you think?" Mizuki said behind his long bangs, poking at the back of the square, black box.

"When I make a little more money," I answered vaguely, as usual. I didn't have a clear goal in mind, and I was worried that I wouldn't be able to make money elsewhere.

"Tomoya, you are greedy." Mizuki wanted to get out of here. I knew that.

"Is it done?" I ignored Mizuki's words. I was a coward.

"Perfection," Mizuki replied.

The yellow and black markings on the chest of his tight-fitting white T-shirt indicated a radiation control zone. It was a sick joke.

"It's on edge." The integrating dosimeters were at a critical juncture.

"It's been four days in a row. It would be strange if it was low."

Even if the number was just below the limit, I could go to work. I was sure the company had applied generous safety margins anyway, so it shouldn't be a problem even if it was a little over.

"I'll be fine." I got o□t of my seat. There was still some time before the meeting, just enough time to brush my teeth and go to the bathroom.

Having left Mizuki sitting at the table and looking out the window in a daze, I went back to my room. From the window of my room, I could see the incinerator towing a pitch-black shadow into the setting sun.

The foreman came to the workers' waiting room and began his nightly roll call. He checked that everyone was present and checked the numbers on the integrating dosimeters that hung around each of the workers' necks. He punched the data into the terminal in his hand. Three workers were instructed to stay in their rooms tonight.

"Silly them, they could have adjusted it a bit," I whispered to Mizuki and got a glare from the foreman. It was easy to adjust the dosimeters if you knew how to do it. But it was forbidden. Because it was dangerous. The foreman knew what we were doing, but as long as we didn't make the numbers too weird, he didn't say anything. It was not easy to get people to work in the field, and if we didn't have eno□gh people, the job wo□ldn't be done by morning.

It was already dark outside the window. "Power transmission stopped. Safety confirmed. Yo□ can start the work," the foreman's radio receiver said. A power-generating satellite in geostationary orbit had stopped power transmission following the decreasing use of electric power at midnight.

"Workstation 3, copy that."

The foreman's language into the radio was always polite. The foreman was also a temporary employee, not a permanent employee. Permanent employees were on the other side of the radio.

"All personnel must wear protective clothing and assemble in front of this vehicle. We're leaving in 30 minutes. Don't forget to check the charge of your helmets. And don't chat in front of me. I'll take half a day off yo□r paycheck if yo□ crap yo□r pants."

The foreman was glaring at me.

"You were stupid," Mizuki said as he put protective tape over the velcro on the front of the suit. The boots, with lead sheets in the soles, were weighty, and the dust masks smelled strange. Still, the daily wage was so high. I would work here, and when I had saved up enough money, I would go into town. I'd always talked about this with Mizuki, who I'd known since junior high school. There were no good jobs in the area.

"You're not putting it in the right place," Mizuki said. He was good at noticing this kind of thing. I shoved the hem of my pants into my boots and wrapped the protective tape around them tightly once more. If I didn't get it neat, the foreman would turn me away, and I would lose my day's earnings.

"Thank you."

"Okay, check me." Mizuki spun around on his right foot, using it as an axis.

"Okay. Perfect." Now me. I spun around once.

"It's perfect," Mizuki said.

I cut the seal on the sticker type dosimeter and put it in place on my chest. Then I looked at the indicator on the helmet and made sure it was fully charged. It was a shared one, but a small skull sticker indicated that I usually used it. Otherwise, it was a pain in the ass to adjust.

Dressed tightly in protective clothing, we left the changing room. In front of the workshop, a microbus with a wide bed in the back was waiting for us. We lined up in front of it. There were twelve of us in total. The foreman, dressed in protective clothing like us, inspected each of us one by one.

"Today, we're going to the Western Thirteenth District. Be sure to report when the dosimeter turns orange. That's a highly polluted area."

The integrating dosimeter that we always wore was designed to display the total exposure in a week. In addition to this, a sticker-type dosimeter on top of our protective clothing kept track of daily exposure. It started in green, then yellow, then orange, then workers had to stop working. If it turned red, the worker had to go to the hospital for a checkup, and he would lose earnings for the days in the hospital.

"Come on. Get in the car."

We boarded the microbus at the behest of the foreman. It was his job to take the wheel, but he did nothing when we arrived at the scene. He just sat in the driver's seat, which was shielded from radiation.

He started driving in the dark. Mizuki and I were sitting in the front seat, so we had a clear view of the outside. The glare from the headlights cut out the concrete road from the dark. The road had been rudely constructed. The workshop itself was in the controlled area, so there was nothing around it. There was nothing but bare ground.

The nuclear accident happened before we were born. It left behind complicated pipes and fuel rods in the core and debris and contaminated soil. In the end, it was decided not to dispose of the low-concentration dirt and debris, and the plant was left as was, with only a dispersal prevention process in place. Of course, it was impossible to simply leave the vast, contaminated area vacant, so it was decided to use it as a receiving grid for a power generation satellite. It was now a significant power generation facility, providing fifteen percent of the metropolitan area's peak power.

I remembered seeing it in a satellite photograph. Only this corner of the archipelago was dark, a gaping hole in the night light.

After a short drive, a vast concrete and metal tree appeared in the light of the headlights. These were the poles of the power grid. Thousands of pillars made up a vast forest. The microbus entered the forest.

The contaminated area where the power receiving grid was located should have been unmanned. If it had needed maintenance, maintenance robots would have been used. If all had gone according to plan, there wouldn't have been any work to do by humans. But there had been an unexpected job.

That was the job of our cleaning team.

First, it was birds. Birds that wandered into the receiving area and were boiled up like a cat in a microwave oven. If it was a common seabird like a seagull or a petrel, it was no problem, but if it was a rare species like an osprey or a goshawk, it was a different story. The power receiving grid itself would be criticized by NGOs who were fussy about environmental protection. So we had to clean up all boiled birds' carcasses before they caused problems. During migration season, one person could collect three large garbage bags of dead birds. That was what we did.

"I have a feeling there will be one today," Mizuki blurted out.

"Do you want to bet?" I said.

"You'll only owe me more."

The losses had been pouring in until now. Mizuki was strangely perceptive about these things.

"I guess I shouldn't. I have a feeling I might have one too."

The conversation froze as we recalled the warning from the foreman. The microbus drove silently through the forest of concrete and metal.

"Here we are. What are you waiting for? Earn your day's wages."

The microbus stopped, and we each grabbed a trash bag and got up from our seats.

When I turned on the light on my helmet, a gray world unfolded in front of me: crushed concrete and rusted steel frames. If I had pointed a Geiger counter at it, it would have sounded like scratching. We started walking in groups through the designated area.

The first object was similar in color to the concrete but different in appearance and texture. The soft gray mass was a seagull. Bending down increased radiation exposure, so I used large metal tongs to pick it up. As my eyes adjusted, I could see more of them. I hadn't been here in maybe two months, and a quick look revealed that quite a few seabirds had fallen since then.

Most of them were gulls and terns. They didn't have the brown feathers of ospreys and goshawks, but there were large unfamiliar birds that had fallen too. There was the carcass of a large black ibis, which must have escaped from a zoo somewhere.

Our flickering lights were all that was visible in the dark concrete forest. Mizuki would be the one closest to me on the right. The distance was too far to talk.

The power receiving grid's struts were arranged in a regular pattern, each one numbered, so there was no need to worry about getting lost. I strained my eyes and looked around to pick up dead birds. The garbage bag in my left hand became heavier and heavier.

When I saw it after midnight, I knew I had been right.

A red boot behind a strut.

"Shit, it's a double suicide."

They were lined up on a blanket, not that old, well boiled but not mummified. A sharp beeping sound echoed in the darkness as I sounded the buzzer hanging from my belt.

"I knew I hit it," Mizuki said, his voice muffled through the dust mask.

"You both are talking nonsense." It was another old worker who said that. Efficiently, he took a few pictures.

There were five people within earshot of the buzzer, and eventually, six workers gathered around the two bodies. Just three of us for each one dead. One of us held both legs while two carried the bodies by their arms.

At some point, the receiving grid had become a suicide spot. They took sleeping pills, and while they slept soundly, the power-generating satellites would transmit microwaves that slowly boiled them. There were no ugly scorch marks on the corpses these days, as the public had been thoroughly informed that all metal had to be removed.

We threw the bodies into the back of the microbus, where several trash bags were already piled. Three workers sat in the bus idly. They were all orange.

"You hit it!" One of them looked back over the seat at Mizuki.

"I was hoping I'd be wrong," Mizuki said with a grumpy voice.

"Don't waste time. Yo□ g□ys go and fill □p a garbage bag quickly. Then we'll leave for today," the foreman declared, and honked the horn of the microbus three times in rapid succession. Then there was a different, sharper so□nd in the darkness. The dosimeter on my chest had t□rned an infinitely yellowish-orange.

When we returned to the workshop, we placed the two bodies on the floor of the morg□e. The cold concrete floor seemed an □ncomfortable place for them to sleep. The police would be there in the morning to take them in, since the foreman would have called them. It wasn't our job to lead them to the scene where the bodies were found. We couldn't and didn't want to know why these two people wanted to die.

Mizuki stood still, looking down at the corpses. I grabbed his elbow and pulled him away. As long as the rumors of a clean death in this place wouldn't die away, there was no stopping suicidal people from scaling the barbed wire fence. The length of one side of the power receiving grid alone was twenty miles.

We returned to the microbus and took the heavy garbage bags to the incinerator behind the workshop. The incinerator would turn the burnt birds into white smoke rising to the sky. But we wouldn't see it because we would be asleep before the sun came up.

"How long are we gonna be here?" Mizuki said, looking down.

"We'll fig□re it o□t. Don't worry abo□t it." I lightly tapped Mizuki on the back.

Once in the workshop, I took off my protective clothing in the changing room. I put my dust mask in place on the shelf and set the helmet on the charger. I shoved the peeled tape, protective clothing, and gloves into a plastic bag and shut the bag tightly. This was going to the incinerator too. They said it had the latest filter, so no radioactive material would be dispersed.

It was a shit terrible job. Even though I was microwave-disinfected, I felt the smell of death seeping into every corner of my body. When I finished, I went to the shower room before anyone else to wash away the smell. I shampooed my hair thoroughly and washed off the fine particles of death.

When I saw a generous amount of hair tangled in the drain, I wondered if it was time to go. Still, if I woke up again, I would probably ask Mizuki to adjust the integrating dosimeter.

I lowered my head under the shower, thinking of the birds returning to heaven in a puff of smoke.

The water, just the right amount of warmth, ran down my neck, down my back, and fell slowly to my feet.

The indelible sin of comfort. When the sun eventually would rise, the grid would begin to send electricity to the city.

The city always forgets the existence of sin.

Takay□ki Ino is a former Japanese government official who now lives with his wife and two cats in Huahin, Thailand.

His first novel won the 2009 Nihon SF new writer award from SF Writers Japan. The award-winning novel, *Oparlia, A Forest Planet*, was published in 2010. Since then, he has published dozens of short stories. His most recent works are "Honest mask" in the anthology *Post Corona SF*, published by Hayakawa Publishing Corporation, "Distance under the Moon Shade" in *Night-land Quarterly*, published by Atelier Third Ltd. and "Kazarov in a Powered Case" in the anthology *Memory of Re-sleeve*, also published by Atelier Third Ltd. (all in Japanese). "The Dragon Sword of Valenharel" is his first English short story in the anthology *Crunchy with Ketchup*, published by WolfSinger Publications.

松島の珊瑚の樹

金子瑠美著

プレストン・グラスマン：訳

海岸線では、鉱物の樹がまるで宝石をちりばめた手のように海から立ち上がり、空に向かって伸びている。さらにその先では、珊瑚の長い枝が波の上で繋がり、鮮やかな赤や青や緑に螺旋を描いている。

今日は世界がやってくる日だ。窓から見えるのは、カメラを降ろして取材場所を決めながら、彼女の到着を待つ報道陣の姿だ。

漁師たちの船が樹の周りに集まり、網やかごを海に投げ入れるのを見ながら、準備をする彼女の隣には夫が立っている。わずか3年前、この海にはかつて地域経済を支えた魚や牡蠣がいなくなり、生態系は崩壊寸前だった。しかし、彼女が開発した塩水電解法と生物工学に基づくサンゴ礁の建設は、その状況を一変させた。波の下のどこかで、鉄筋や金網のミネラル豊富な陰極にサンゴの破片を固定し、新しい生態系を育てているのだ。

「ミオは誇れるものがたくさんあるね。」とタケシは言う。彼はこの樹やサンゴ礁が、単なるコンセプト・ドローイングや走り書きのメモに過ぎなかったことを今でも覚えている。しかし、地震や嵐、隣国との戦争に耐え、妻の生涯の夢はサンゴ礁のように大きくなった。

彼女は母にもらった贈り物をポケットから取り出し、指で回しながら「ケイコに見せてあげたいわ」と言う。それは、ミオの似顔絵を彫った珊瑚のかけらであった。母は自分の体調が悪くなっていっても、街が元気になるのを見て誇らしげにしていた。「私があなたにあげられるのはこれだけなの。」そう言いながら母は娘に珊瑚のかけらを手渡した。「でも、これには私の愛と夢と希望が詰まっているの。いつか、大切な人に渡してあげてね。」

彼女は最初それが理解できず、絶対に手放さない、ずっと持っているとケイコに言った。しかし、その時彼女は、自分の将来に希望を感じている母の言葉の意味を理解した。

窓の外には、松島海岸の島々の間に色とりどりの珊瑚がモザイクのように広がっている。波が樹々にぶつかると、その衝撃のたびに鉄筋網の芯にエネルギーのパルスが伝わり、サンゴの構造体が波の下で成長し続けるために必要な出力が生み出されるのだ。

「彼女は、君がここで成し遂げたことを誇りに思うだろうね。」とタケシは言う。

「母がいなければ、私はここにいなかったわ。」彼女は、洪水や飢饉、長年にわたって生き残るために苦労した母の話を思い出しながら言う。彼女が生まれる数カ月前、父と兄は海に流された。母は家を失い、東京の従姉妹に10年間世話になったが、松島に帰って再起を図ることだけを願っていた。

ミオも同じように、母の夢を無駄にしたくないという思いに動かされた。そして、母が誇りに思うであろう、海から立ち上がる自給自足の逞しい都市がここにあった。

鏡に映る自分を見る。うっすらと白髪が混じり、目尻にはシワが寄っている。こんなところにいたのね、ケイコ。と彼女は思う。

タケシは海の向こうを指差して、「ほら、あの家並みをごらんよ」と言う。「よく育っているね。」

新しくできた家々の長い列が海から顔を出しているのが見える。先日の津波の後、何千人もの住民がすでにバイオロックの家屋に住んでおり、さらに多くの人が必要としている。ほんの数年前までは、1キロワット時の電力で0.4〜1.5キログラムの成長が可能だったが、新しいバイオエンジニアリングの手法により、その速度が加速された。今では、牡蠣の殻のように波打ち際で成長している。成熟したら海から引き上げ、家のない人々に提供するのだ。

今、海岸沿いには撮影隊が集まっていて、鉱物を塗った板の上で米などの作物を育てている浮き畑の映像を撮っている。

「彼らが待ってるわ。」と彼女は言う。

彼は「一緒にいるよ。」と言いながら、彼女の手に手を伸ばす。

彼女は母の贈り物を再び指で回す。母の愛、母の夢、母の都市への希望。

「私もあなたと一緒にいるわ。」と彼女は言い、夫の手に珊瑚の破片を置く。

そして、彼女は世界に立ち向かう力を得るのだった。

R□mi Kaneko has been working in the film and TV ind□stry in Japan for several years. She has written screenplays and a novel called *Good Morning Jupiter*, which is currently being translated by Preston Grassmann. Her recent translated work has appeared in *The Unquiet Dreamer: A Tribute to Harlan Ellison* by PS Publishing and *Out of the Ruins* by Titan.

The Coral Trees of Matsushima

Rumi Kaneko

Translated from Japanese by Preston Grassmann

Along the shoreline, the mineral trees have risen from the sea like jeweled hands reaching for the sky. Further out, long branches of coral have joined above the waves, spiraling together into bright red and blue and green—fingers crossed for some imagined future.

Today is the day the world will come. From the window, she can see the media unloading cameras, plotting locations for coverage as they wait for her to arrive.

Her husband stands next to her as she prepares, watching the boats of fishermen gather around the trees, throwing nets and cages into the sea. Only three years ago, the ecosystem had nearly collapsed, the seas empty of the fish and oysters that once built their local economy. But her methods of salt-water electrolysis and bioengineered reef construction have changed all of that. Somewhere below the waves, grafters are fixing coral fragments to the mineral-rich cathodes of rebar and wire-mesh, enabling a new ecosystem to grow.

"You have a lot to be proud of, Mio," Takeshi says. He can still remember when the trees and the reefs were nothing more than concept drawings, scribbled notes on pages. But they had risen out of that dream, enduring quakes and storms and the wars of neighboring countries, his wife's lifelong ambition growing like the reef itself.

"I wish Keiko was here to see it," she says, taking her mother's gift out of her pocket and turning it through her fingers: a fragment of coral carved into her own likeness. She remembers how proud her mother had been, watching the city grow back to life, even as her own health had been failing. "This is all I can give you," she had said, handing her daughter the coral piece. "But it contains all my love, my dreams, and my hopes. Someday you'll pass it on, give it to someone you care about."

She hadn't □nderstood that at first, telling Keiko that she would never let it go, that she would hold onto it forever. But then she realized what her mother had meant—inspiration had to endure.

From her window, she looks further out, where colored corals weave together like a mosaic between the islands of the Matsushima coastline. Out there, the waves surge against the trees, each impact sending a pulse of energy down through a rebar-mesh core to generate the output required for her coral structures to continue growing below the waves.

"She would've been proud of what you've accomplished here," Takeshi says.

"I wouldn't be here without her," she says, remembering her mother's stories of floods and famine, of str□ggling to s□rvive for so many years. A few months before she was born, Keiko's father and brother had been swept away by the sea. Her mother had been left without a home, cared for by her cousins in Tokyo for ten years, but all she'd wanted was to return to Matsushima so she could rebuild.

Mio had been driven by that same need, and for her mother's dream not to be in vain. And here was something she would've been pro□d of, a city rising o□t of the sea itself, self-s□fficient and strong.

She looks at herself in the mirror. There's a light threading of gray hair now and creases in the corners of her eyes. *There you are, Keiko*, she thinks.

"Look at all those houses," Takeshi says, pointing out to another part of the sea. "They're growing very well."

A long row of newly formed houses can be seen emerging from the sea. After the recent tsunami, thousands of local residents are already living in bio-rock homes and many more are needed. Only a few years ago, every kilowatt hour of electricity would produce .4 to 1.5 kilograms of growth, but with new methods of bioengineering, that rate has been accelerated. Now, they grow below the waves like shells in an oyster bed. When they reach maturity, they'll be lifted out of the sea and given to those without homes.

She notices a film-crew gathering along the shore now, taking footage of the floating farms, where rice and other crops are growing on mineral encrusted plates.

"They're waiting," she says.

"I'll be with you," he says, reaching out for her hand.

She turns her mother's gift through her fingers again—her love, her dreams, her hope for what their city could become.

"And I'll be with you," she says, placing the coral piece in her husband's hand.

It gives her strength as she turns to face the world.

Preston Grassmann is a Shirley Jackson Award-nominated editor, writer, and translator. His most recent work has been published in *Nature Magazine*, *Strange Horizons*, *PS Publishing*, and *Titan*. He is a regular contributor to Nature and currently lives in Japan, where he is working on several new projects, including a book of illustrated stories with Yoshika Nagata.

Crisis

Jesse Nee-Vogelman

We are not doing anything about it because we have to help our parents pay their mortgage. We are not doing anything about it because the children want dogs to play with. We are not doing anything about it because I cannot stop thinking about a girl I sat and watched at a coffee shop six subway stops away. We are not doing anything because who believes that stuff anyway? When I close my eyes I do not see oceans breaking over Miami or San Francisco but green eyes from a sooty dream in a café. We are not doing anything about it because her hair is dark and heavy like carbon dioxide and likewise pungent and cloudy by memory. We are not because it's too hot in the summer. We are not doing anything about the world of our children and grandchildren because we have not made them yet. I want a family and three children and a yard and a gabled roof. We are not doing anything because all I can think of is sex. We are hungry students. We are poor. We are not doing anything about it because she answered the phone and said yes and we met at the café where I first saw her and we went for a long walk near the river and that day we could not imagine the footprints we made would one day fill with water and the sediment of youth. We are not doing anything about it because I am writing a novel. I have work tomorrow. I found a job forging college essays for teenagers. They are thinking about the future. We are saving money to travel the world and see the endangered places tipping into the edge. We are not doing anything about it because she hasn't answered her phone in a week and the space between rings and the rings are the rising knife of not her. I am distracted. I cannot read news articles like this. I cannot feel guilty like this. We are not doing anything about it because I want to own a home and pay bills and eat cereal in the morning and wake up to her on her side facing away from me knowing she has not moved in the night. I want to make enough money to buy her happiness as best I can. We are not doing anything about it because we have to pay our mortgage. There's a new cell phone out. APR is lower for Christmas deals. We are not doing anything about it because I usually take public transportation. I use CFL bulbs and wash my clothes in cold water. We are not doing anything about it because she has put on weight. Her hips and breasts are round like the curve of her lips. We are not doing anything about it because she's sick. We are not doing anything about it because she looks beautiful in white. Like a fragile rounded egg. We are not doing anything about it because we are on vacation. We just bought gym memberships. I have to clean. While making protein shakes I heard a gasp from the bedroom and spilled yolk and powder across the floor. We are not doing anything abo□t it beca□se it's a boy and he has ten toes and ten fingers and cried when the doctor held him and he already looks like me. We are not doing anything about it because we live inland. We are not doing anything about it because I don't mind mosquitoes. We are not doing anything about it because our baby is sick and hospitals need fuel and electricity and that is where our baby is. This is now the land of our children. But our children want dogs to play with. We are not doing anything about it because his hair is soft and hot like molten string. Outside on the pavement our grandchildren fry eggs in the sun. We are not doing anything about it because where are the car keys? We are not doing anything because sometimes at night her thighs remind me of her thighs years ago. It's trash night. There is going to be a storm and the Bhatnagars need to trim the rotten branches on their linden tree. There is a book I might read. I'm starting that diet again. Her father's funeral ran late. We are taking continuing education courses on kitchen sanitation at the community college. I haven't had coffee yet. We are not doing anything about it because Harold is sick. The Bhatnagars invited us over for dinner. We're vegetarians now. But she's staying late at work again. I spend my afternoons remembering how I used to play baseball in the field behind my ho□se where b□ms lived in deserted d□go□ts. We are not doing anything because our friends are dying from other things: cancer is bad Lyme is bad high cholesterol is bad car accidents are bad alcohol poisoning is bad suicide is bad. We are not doing anything because I do not actually believe she will sign the papers. I have not slept well for thirty-two years. We are not because I stubbed my toe on the new Ikea desk that I will use to do my writing about which I had forgotten but it's not too late yet. There's still all the potential in the world. I was twenty-three years old, once, you know. I want to, but I don't think we will. I want to, but I have work tomorrow.

Jesse Nee-Vogelman is a graduate of Harvard College and the University of Montana's fiction MFA program. There, he received the university's highest creative writing award, the Merriam-Frontier Prize. His work has been published in the *New Haven Review* and the *Harvard Advocate*, where his story won the Louis Begley Prize, selected by Jamaica Kincaid. Previously, he served as the Artist-in-Residence at Harvard's Signet Society of Arts and Letters. He currently lives in Montana and has a cat and a dog.

What's To Like?

Al Simmons

A granite sk⊡ll rose from the desert floor,
symbol of our demise,
in the 115 degree searing Egyptian heat.

We took a selfie with the Sphinx
for the fun of it, and titled it,
our seven thousand mile carbon footprint.

And then, we were off to Paris, to dine
near the Spanish Steps, and
post a photo of our dinner on FB.

From Paris to our favorite restaurant in Seattle
for clams, before clams die out.
Remember clams? Their beds forever buried deep
beneath the oil slick. What a pity, such a waste
when the pipes burst.
How many miles and tanks of gas lost,
spoiled, ruined?

Buenos Aires for breakfast with our dear friends.
But mostly, what we do is eat delicious meals
prepared with imported ingredients
from home sweet home.

Do you like my website, how we wrecked the world?
That's me, the amateur ecologist standing
before the Sphinx
in the land of dead pharaohs and pyramids.

Al Simmons has been quoted on the front page of The New York Times. Poet-In-Residence, City of Chicago, 1979-80. Founder of The World Heavyweight Poetry Championship Fights, Chicago/Taos, New Mexico, 1979-2001. Nominated for a 2021 SFPA's Rhysling Award. His work has appeared in 35 journals, magazines and anthologies since January 2017, including *Forage, Your Impossible Voice, Star 82 Review, Alcyone, A Magazine of Speculative Fiction*, Issues II & III, *Former People Journal, The Sum Journal, Rune Bear Magazine, Genre: Urban Arts, Thin Air, Red Coyote, Heron Clan VII, Kanstellation Magazine, Abyss and Apex*, Issue 76, *Art In The Age of Covid-19*, and *The Martian Wave*, Hiraeth Publishing. He lives in Alameda, California. See more at simmonsink.blogspot.com.

Tyrni

Laura Adrienne Brady

We were prickling
pine   we were h⊡mming
horn   we were sand
sm⊡dged   by sea
we were weed   wrapped
and swallowed   antler crowned
h⊡m of r⊡bythroat   before we were

White   is not a color is   the absence

a res⊡lt of o⊡r eyes   the reflection

a scatter

of everything

Here is where we lost   o⊡r moon
songs   o⊡r fox   tale rooted dance
how to say   *sandthorn*   *sallowthorn*   *sea buckthorn*

Tyrni

Where to find orange flecked
fr⊡it   how to snake
arm thro⊡gh thorns   cl⊡tch
avoid the colorless   b⊡ry
fingers in flesh   the ripest sq⊡ish
o⊡tstretched   j⊡iced
See how my hands   remember
the weight of this   kind of gold

Laura Adrienne Brady is an MFA candidate at Northern Arizona University and a writer, educator, and singer-songwriter (known as Wren). Laura's poems and essays have appeared in *Brevity*, *The Rappahannock Review*, on Seattle city buses, and elsewhere. Her most recent project, *Pink Stone: Songs from Moose Lodge*, is a folk album of original songs and a paired companion book of essays, lyrics, photos, and illustrations. Supported by a 4Culture Art Projects Grant, the collection explores illness, intimacy, and relationship with land, set against the backdrop of Washington's Methow Valley. Explore Laura's music and writing at SwimmingRabbitArts.com.

A Little More Kindness

Prashanth Srivatsa

From space, the planet appeared blue-green and lonely. The Manithan decelerated through re-entry, exchanging speed for heat. I remained stretched in my pressure suit, suffering the shudders. Rajini lay beside me, emitting a series of blinks on the panel across his chest that reassured me the insulation cloaking our chamber was sufficient to withstand the plasma pummeling us from outside.

I'd made the photobot. His conviction was my handiwork. All those years cloaked in the warehouses of Arya-7, forcibly away from Alekha who was alone in the colony beneath the bridges reserved for the caste-less.

Seven generations of my family had been raised confined in those colonies, laboring through sludge and waste and the sweat of those who couldn't prove their castes.

I gripped my unfinished letter to Alekha as the Manithan juddered in entry. Rajini tinkered with the controls. We had no planned landing site. It was near impossible to find one on an Earth ravaged by untamed wilderness and abandoned for four hundred and eighty seven years.

As the pummeling ceased, though, and the Manithan burst through layers of clouds, the father in me subsided and the photographer in me jerked awake.

I gaped even as my hands folded the letter back inside my pocket, while Rajini activated the trackers.

Earth. Beautiful, savage, ruthless Earth. Enduring in our absence. No—thriving. The jungle sprawled below us in spikes of unhindered growth, and as the Manithan sped across the skies, the seas blossomed out of land much like what we voyaged over back in the colonies, but so much more serene, so much more . . . regal.

I hesitated to get out my camera. Rajini, beside me, already commissioned for the same, was capturing the panorama. I was only baggage, the unwantedness of whose presence Rajini never held back from expressing every few hours, reminding me of the option laid out in front of me—to return. Return and remain beside my daughter who had come to love Rajini more than me. Who laughed at his quirks as much as she hated my time away from her in the warehouses, to a point where any effort at reconciliation appeared to be a pittance.

This illegal journey would be my apology. From securing a job in the endless grind of the warehouses to learning to build photobots and re-programming Rajini to condone my presence on a journey meant exclusively for the likes of him—every second away from Alekha in the last seven years had been dedicated to the singular purpose of smuggling myself into a ship bound for Earth.

Alekha and I were now one trip away from moving out of the colonies beneath the bridges forever.

"What is our destination?" I asked Rajini.

His chrome setup gyrated towards me. "We make for any airstrip around Delhi. My commission informs me of seven monuments within a two hundred mile radius of the capital that are worthy of significance to the Library and Universities in Arya-7. We begin there."

"Including the Taj Mahal, no doubt," I muttered, just loud enough for him to hear.

"Obviously."

"Overrated marble junk," I offered politely.

I had seen the pictures. The gallery of heritage sites and monuments whose images were captured before evacuation for the future generations to assimilate as remnants of their erstwhile home. As an example of marble architecture, the Taj Mahal was all right—I remembered rolling my eyes the first time and scoring it five and a half out of ten—but as one of seven wonders of the old world? Blasphemy. There were far more intricately carved temples and monuments in India worthy of that honor. Monuments not built by slaves who were blinded and had their fingers chopped off upon completion.

History, sadly, was not objective.

"I have my orders, sir," Rajini said. My programming, with the quiet exception of my intrusion in this ship, had to conform to the regulations of the photobot codes. Rajini had executed half a dozen round trips to Earth under the command of a senior photobot before he could captain his own ship. This was his first solo. I was unsure how torn he was between a sense of achievement and annoyance.

"Of course," I told him, secretly proud of how far he'd come. "Go on."

The Delhi airstrip was unrecognizable. The wilderness had consumed it, as it had consumed all of Delhi, undoing centuries of engineering and toil. The Manithan whistled over the ruin. Beneath me, failed foundations and tumbled buildings were replaced with buckthorns and birches invading the crushed concrete. Roots heaved up sidewalks and split sewers until they furrowed the lanes and everything around them.

Rajini charted a course for an alternate landing site in Agra. I silenced my groan, put on some music in my headphones and promptly fell asleep.

Rajini nudged me awake with an alarm beep I was too familiar with from back beneath the bridges in Arya-7.

Light dazzled through the frame of the Manithan, and as Rajini steered the nose downward, I glimpsed the Taj Mahal choked in ivy and fern, one minaret altogether non-existent, the other three cracked or fallen into r□bble, s□nlight filtering into the dark within. I imagined the ruins echoed with the croak of frogs breeding in streams teeming with mahseers and trouts, and mussels dropped by seagulls in the lake that now thrived without the poison of washermen.

This was not waste. This was the life that the humans had refused to co-exist with during my ancestors' time.

"You're lucky." Rajini's voice box let out a chuckle. I wondered what his sarcasm meter was tuned to. "The monument is beyond identification. Res□lts from my recordings state it does not f□lfill the criteria for the End□rance Project."

I hated the Taj Mahal simply for its popularity among the colonies, b□t for the first time, I disagreed in defense of it.

"It's beautiful," I mouthed, the breath escaping in a curling wisp. At the peak of its decadence, the Taj Mahal had represented something glorious, disparate from the tortured hands that had raised it. "Let me down, I need to get a picture from up close."

Rajini let out a guttural beep. "That would be foolish, sir. And not recommended at all."

"Yes, yes. I appreciate your warning. You've a heart of gold. Now let me down, Rajini. I have my pressure suit, insulated and completely sealed. You have scanned the area. There's no viral presence, nor is there any radiation from the Narora power plant, which is...", I glanced at the charts, "no less than a hundred and fifty kilometres away."

Rajini appeared to process my response. In the end, there was only a muffled moan.

"I don't understand why you had to accompany me in the first place, sir." He stopped just short of expressing disapproval. "An image-grabbing mission has never occurred that wasn't exclusively conducted by geo-satellites or photobots. Your presence is... making things awkward for me. I am questioning my limits."

The Arya-7 engineer override. Rajini's professional boundaries obscured his personal inclination for Alekha's and my safety, coded beneath layers like a smudge.

For the first time since we broke into the atmosphere, the photographer pushed his seat back and allowed the father to lean forward. The father in me was a mild-mannered man, stocked with memories and longing and an ache to merge the past with the present. "I promised Alekha I would show her a picture of our ancestral home. This is the only way."

If Rajini knew my true purpose, he'd abandon his mission and dispatch a signal of compromise back to Arya-7. I was aware of the failings of my own creation.

"So you admit this is illegal?"

I sighed. "You won't be decommissioned, if that's what you're worried about. The modification chip was inserted post the control checks for tolerance. Arya-7 can be really blind sometimes, you know."

"All this for for a few pictures?" Rajini asked.

"That's it." I straightened my lips and gestured to him to unlock the pod's exit.

"You abandoned her in Arya-7," he said flatly. The fact of it stung me, the word 'abandoned' lying in the air between us, cold and static. "Her survival rate dips by 6.5 percent in your absence."

I was aware of the risk. "She has neighbors in the colonies, and friends."

Lies. She had nobody.

"Why are you here, sir?"

I ran a hand into my pockets, feeling the soft touch of parchment. "I want my daughter to know who my ancestors were and where they lived. Is that too much to ask?"

Rajini did not reply. I laid a hand on his metallic shoulder, feeling the nanites within squirm and rearrange. "It's just a few photos. We don't have to do it now. We can keep it for the end, once we're done with all the monuments."

He only gave the briefest of nods before landing the Manithan on the patch of overgrown land, once the I of the Taj Mahal. I pulled the latch on the pod. A hiss and groan gave way to sunlight streaming in beams of dust. I wore the camera like a garland and ambled out, Rajini on my tail.

"Follow my lead, sir," he said, one of his eye sockets rotating like a camera lens to unleash layers of focus, gleaming under the afternoon sun.

Acid rain had pocked most of the marble on the surface of Shah Jehan's dedication to Mumtaz. From behind the Taj Mahal and across the narrow river, acres of woodland straddled the border. Groves of ash rose above an understory of ferns and massive birches and old banyans, bridging the river, their army of vines creeping up the walls of the Taj Mahal and shrouding it in a matted veil of thorn, tangled briars and withies. The smell of wisteria and honeysuckle, or so I imagined within the suit. I lifted the camera to my eyes and captured the side of the broken monument and the jungle mounting it. Retaliation, I named the picture.

In any unstricken, abandoned part of the world, Rajini and I would have to be wary of lairs of corrupted wolves, bears and coyotes even in the midst of a choked megalopolis. Initial attempts to return had resulted in attacks by mutated species clinging to life. I imagined what it would be like to have that virus course through my bloodstream, pick out strands of my cells and twist them into something malicious and unforgiving. Desperate and alone.

I'd glanced through reports of New York and Paris. And of Kuala Lumpur and Hong Kong. The predictor model had been quashed fifteen years into our evacuation.

Ah, the evacuation. If only my ancestors hadn't been so hasty! If only they hadn't left it behind.

I checked the viral meter again and was contented with a below-threshold signature. Indication of a severely truncated fauna. Whatever remained would have had to overcome repeated bouts of illnesses and atrophy. Chances were slim.

Rajini stopped forty feet from the entrance to the Taj Mahal—now a caved-in remnant of an arch. It reminded me of Buland Darwaza, which I preferred over this blanched dullness. The photobot raised his head—a series of clicks detonated around his eye in capturing the monument. I walked a few paces to the side, away from Rajini's lengthening shadow, and held my own camera to my eye. The dark entrance, the cobwebs, the arching vines, the silence. The history erased and rebuilt by nature.

Click.

I named this image Better Dead than Alive.

The suit was suffocating. I was desperate to be rid of it, but despite the safety signals, there was no way Rajini would have permitted me to strip. There was a time before the photobot missions when he'd walk ahead of Alekha and me through the colonies, never letting anyone get close except those with whom we shared the pain. Now? Now was different. Rajini was not fully mine. Only Alekha was. I intended to keep it that way.

"Was it better the last time you were here?" I asked, as we strolled back towards the Manithan an hour later.

Rajini slowed his pace to allow me to catch up with him. We trod on high grass, the rectangular pool the Taj Mahal overlooked now entirely drowned in vegetation. "It was three years ago when I visited with Senior Kamal. So, no. Much, much worse. Some of the obscenities were still standing."

"Come on, be serious."

"I am," he replied. "Contrary to your inputs, the Arya-7 engineers further programmed me to be ecologically oriented. Just because we are clothed in metal does not mean our minds cannot be tempered to care for soil."

I looked around, at the diminishing state of humanity's footsteps in that desolate wasteland of Agra. "Give it a few hundred years. After all the genetic degradation, they'll stop sending you here. There won't be anything left of our legacy to capture and study."

"Quite the contrary, sir," Rajini rolled over the ramp of our ship. "It becomes all the more necessary to visit this place once nature's takeover is complete. It will be a reminder of what once was and what could have been, and that acts of humanity forced them to depart between those two states of time."

"There was bound to be compromise," I said. "It's impractical for humans to be dominated completely by nature."

"And yet," he stopped to splay his aluminum limbs wide, bolts creaking. "Look who has come out on top."

"Humans adapted," I countered.

Rajini hissed. "To adapt and abandon is to be left with no choice."

I was unsure if this existential dread was of my making, but I avoided questioning him further. I had come to realize that Rajini had…evolved since his inception in the feeble light of the warehouses. With each passing day, I had fewer and fewer options to modify in him. He was, in the end, a property of Arya-7, and I was only a royalty-earner who'd once tightened the screws. I feared the day was not far off when he'd walk into the colonies beneath the bridges and fail to recognize Alekha. Or worse, harm her.

I stopped, lifted the camera and my eyes and captured the bent metallic frame of Rajini as his silhouette lingered at the entrance to the Manithan, against a backdrop of the domination of jungle. I shrugged off my fears and named this image Guardian.

We visited Fatehpur Sikhri to capture the Buland Darwaza—the red and buff sandstone withered, the chhatris atop it enduring through the carnage on the ground. Greenery had swallowed up the arched entrance before flowing into the courtyard of the jama masjid. The spandrels of white marble had eroded without maintenance, gnawed at by creepers aiming for the cusped ornament at the tip of the dome.

The structure itself, though, could be recognized for what it was—a gaping maw of a door chewed by bracken. It passed Rajini's obscure metrics and earned a photograph. I took one, too, kneeling fifty feet from the door, capturing its height and width, then zoomed at the only Persian inscription that hadn't faded: He who hopes for a day may hope for eternity, but the World endures but an hour.

I named the picture A Dead Door in a Living Planet.

The other monuments in Delhi—Humayun's Tomb, the Qutub Minar, the India Gate and Safdarjung Tomb—had been completely submerged in the overflowing arm of the jungle, as though Earth had longed to cover up its errors and return to its state of origin at the earliest convenience.

"Where to next?" I asked Rajini, once the thrusters lifted us off. It had begun to grow dark outside, and no amount of comforting viral metrics would make me want to remain down in that wilderness.

Rajini seemed to analyze the guidance system, one eye roving at the vitals of the air outside. "I believe the Sun Temple in Konark is our next stop. Along the coast of the Bay of Bengal. Before we head south to Rameshwaram."

Rameshwaram was near my hometown. My heart began to beat just a little quicker. "Sounds like a plan," I said, before curling up on my seat and submitting to music once again.

We found a barren hilltop to land our vessel for the night, where sleep rushed to overcome me. Rajini stayed awake, analyzing the pictures taken, transmitting them back to Arya-7, and pretending to be busy. I knew he was waiting for me to react to being the only living human being on Earth at that moment. I didn't, rather forcefully. Lest he get the impression that I was not suited to the neutral demands of this mission. The feeling never escaped me that Rajini was constantly looking to test me and my own limits. I was a bug in his otherwise perfect routine of interstellar travel and image-grabbing.

In truth, I did not wish to disappoint him.

Come morning, we landed in Konark, in the courtyard of the Sun Temple. The rekha deul—the main sanctuary of the temple—had been swallowed up entirely. The ground had cratered beneath a couple of sanctums and mandapas. The temple had already been half a ruin in colonial years. What survived had been bulldozed by weeds and torrents of underbrush, the Khondalite stone's faster weathering accelerating the decay.

I felt a pang of pity. The sanctum's raha rose above the pavilion, the sole, unsullied part of the temple, which, to Rajini, seemed worthy of a picture.

Otherwise, he was quiet. He rolled ahead into the ruin while I lazily followed him in my uncomfortable suit, stopping to take pictures of the carved stones, the walls ornamented with reliefs, the erotic sculptures and the stone wheels engraved in the pillars—slowly subjected to their end.

Ten minutes later, Rajini said urgently, "The inside of the sanctum is unsafe. We must return to the ship."

The main temple and the jaganmohana porch lay within the sanctum.

"Come on," Rajini urged me. "This is non-negotiable."

I did not resist. We shuttled away, the indicators on Rajini's chest glowing a faint amber, emitting a sonorous beep that faded as we gained altitude. "The corrosion on the walls interfered with my sensors until we were on the courtyard," he justified, while I stretched my legs over the cockpit. "There are mutations down there within the sanctum.... I apologize. I put you in danger."

I blinked and folded my legs. "You have nothing to apologize for, relax. I still have my suit on, if you noticed."

"Irrespective," he mumbled. "The well-being of the crew is my responsibility."

Silence roosted between us for hours. Most of it I drowned in half a bottle of whiskey while filtering through my pack for the old letters that had pointed to my family's ancestral home. I read them and re-read them until the words of my forefathers echoed in my ears. A distant calling I had ignored for years. Only now, with a daughter ostracized and stranded without a roof in Arya-7, I desperately responded to it. None of the seven generations before me had. They could not, not without the resource piloting the ship next to me, each minute growing more suspicious.

Rameshwaram lay submerged beneath the ocean. Only the ornate, sculpted tops of a handful of temples floated overland in a colony of reeds and driftwood. Paddies were barely discernible, transformed into pockets of marsh. Boats lay overturned around parts of the inner town that still lingered on the surface.

Rajini appeared satisfied.

"No photos," he beamed, once the statistics confirmed what I had already concluded from his limited offering of metal-tinged expressions. "The monuments are beyond capturing. I hereby declare our mission complete, sir."

"Well, yours, yes," I interjected hopefully.

Rajini ignored me. "I can lower the hatch to allow you a couple of pictures, if you desire. This is magnificent. I only wish I had the permission to soak in this scene of the natural domination of our mother."

I was tempted to remind him that I was his mother.

I stood on the precipice of the Manithan's exit, one hand gripping the railing, the other clasping the camera through the gloves of my suit.

The pictures turned out remarkably well. I even managed to zoom in on a colony of red-crowned cranes, those revered portents of peace, gliding over bulrushes in perfect formation.

When I returned to my seat, Rajini regarded me with careful precision. I imagined if he had human eyes, they would have narrowed, and if he had human lips, they would have curled to utter his next words in a patronizing monotone.

"Valliyur, is it?"

I gulped, trying to regain my composure. My ancestral hometown.

"Yes."

"You will have fifteen minutes."

"Thank you," I blurted.

From hovering over the debris of Rameshwaram to the soaked jungles of Valliyur took us less than an hour. Along the way, my eyes roved over the thriving wilderness beneath us. Civilization had ended, and I had little emotion to spare.

Out there on Arya-7, faith was geographically challenged. It came out twisted and misshapen, its roots on Earth long forgotten. We had to submit proof of caste to be eligible for a roof. The ones who couldn't were given the colonies beneath the bridges, where death was but a hiss away. I told myself what I always told Alekha: the spirits of the gods we prayed to were too distant for our screaming hymns and chants.

I need not have tried to guide Rajini across the plains towards the speck of Valliyur using the stained map in my hand, the territory familiar only in name and in the haunting of memories. The forests once bordering Valliyur had swept over the town. In fact, until Rajini pointed at an accidental clearing, I couldn't tell that I was home.

When we touched down, the sensors began to flare.

"Ignore it," I bumbled, in a hurry.

"The parameters are over the threshold by four percent, sir. The Kundakulam Nuclear Facility is less than eighty kilometres away. There is leaked radioactivity. And there's definite presence of virulent particles in the air."

"I have my suit. You promised me fifteen minutes," I said. I imagined Alekha shivering beside the fires alone these last four months. Clinging to hope, clinging to the idea of Rajini and me returning. How much longer before her disappointment in me transformed into indifference? How much longer before she was forced down the path of many around her who sneaked into tents and crouched in the shadows of the sludges to steal and kill? Her caste should not have mattered. And yet, so far from Earth and its pious atmosphere, it mattered more than ever. Arya-7 had been constructed on the societal evils that should have been left behind like the millions who couldn't make it into the shuttles.

Rajini's head vibrated in a formidable shake.

I gulped. "I . . . I need to do this. Please. It's for my daughter. Sh-she does not deserve the bridges. Ten minutes. Just ten."

A signal choked out of Rajini. "It's a poisoned land, sir. It is my priority to safeguard your life and the life of any crew on board."

"Five minutes," I begged. "Maybe fewer given there's a good chance my ancestor's house does not even exist anymore. It's probably all jungle already. Let me just check."

The improbability of the existence of my ancestral home at least temporarily stumped Rajini. I suspected the sentiment about my daughter, the first honest statement I had uttered to Rajini since smuggling myself into the Manithan, had no impact.

After a long moment, his sensors changed color.

"Five minutes," he repeated. "Just photos."

I nodded in relief and pressed the button to release the hatch. The other hand I held to my chest where my bloated suit's outer pocket contained the letters.

"Tighten your seals, sir," Rajini added as I strode past him and down the ramp.

Home was a clusterfuck of tangled wood and leaves. The co-ordinates on the letters matched the location where I stood. Around me, a few collapsed houses. I did not know if one of them belonged to my ancestors. There had been a name and number on the gate four hundred and eighty seven years ago. Plot 11. Pavithra.

The walls were buried under a thick knot of briars. I skulked around like a fox, the suit increasingly a hindrance to my need. Ahead, more broken homes. Roofs caved in. Gates overgrown in tendrils of greenery. Vines enveloping entire floors. Branches piercing the windows of cars. Leaves breathing everywhere. There was so much life it was overwhelming.

Ahead, I glimpsed a wall still standing. I crept closer, crawling through a hole and tumbling out on the other side, clearing condensation from my visor before squinting at the inscription on the wall.

The 11 had been scr□bbed off. Only the 'itra' remained of the name.

Home.

I lifted the camera and held it against the suit's visor. Click. I named the image Legacy. Another click. Purpose. A third, of the verandah and the porch leading to a door scratched and holed into darkness. A Gift to a Daughter.

My five min□tes were □p. I glanced back and my breath caught as I realized I had walked almost a hundred metres from the Manithan. It was barely visible through the thick forest cover.

I climbed the wall and bundled inside the home. Gave the door the barest of nudges and watched it collapse. Pollen rose from the floor in an oppressive clo□d. The walls were wet; the floor was wet; the banisters on the stairs were wet. The boots attached to the suit's membrane were moisture-proof but wet. I climbed the stairs, two at a time, wet and lost and full of longing for a world I had no part in either creating or destroying.

There were three rooms on the first floor. I waded into the smallest, where I hoped they'd buried their greatest secrets. Coated in brambles and ivy. Branches broke through the lone window, leaves of the banyan as large as coracles. Insects crawling upon them. An owl hooted in the distance.

The roof had began to cave in. Cracks on the floor. A cratered sink on one end. The bed had broken and lay a ruin. Only a safe endured at the end of the room, as though it had been moved in yesterday.

Sheesham at first touch. I traced its contours and then, using the code from my letters, opened its drawers. More letters, untouched for centuries but preserved. And a document. I opened it.

A will.

Immediate transfer of property to the colony, drafted post the accords and after the evacuation ships had been prepared. My heart galloped, my hands tracing an inlaid wooden box that lay beneath the forgotten will. I pocketed the letters and the document, then lifted the box. It felt heavy in my hand.

The latch clicked open at my touch. Inside lay an ancient pocket watch, with a man's and a woman's face shaded in sepia, the dials stuck at twenty seven minutes past nine. A necklace beneath it, and a smaller box of turmeric and sacred ash. And dried sandal-wood paste. Worthless in Arya-7. Just a memory, preserved and then abandoned under the duress of an emergency. And yet, it was suddenly everything. Worth a journey through hyperspace, through a fiery atmosphere, past submerged cities and ruined temples and monuments with their histories erased. I glanced through the will once again and smiled. I could easily prove my ancestry. The names would suffice. Alekha suddenly had a line connecting her to this ruin. A malignant caste that ought to have been erased. Our lives in Arya-7 depended on it.

I placed the box in the largest pocket of the suit and zipped it up.

Then I turned to leave, and froze.

The beast at the door had been a wolf at some point, of that I was certain. What the virus had mutated it into I did not have a name for. It snarled at me from beneath the doorway, drooling, teeth as long and sharp as kitchen knives. It had no hair, only rough, bronze skin, pockmarked and swollen, with pus releasing every few seconds as it breathed.

It took one step inside, and I backed away, tripping and falling, fortunately, only over the broken bed's frame. My elbow made a crunching sound, but my fear was reserved for the monstrosity looming in front of me.

When it leaped, I closed my eyes.

The sound of the bullet exploding across the chamber filled my ears and my chest, setting the heart cornered in it ablaze. I opened my eyes and watched the beast stagger, stumble, and fall two feet from me, a gaping hole in the back of its head, black blood seeping out in a miasma of all that was wrong.

Rajini stood in the doorway.

"You're late," he said. I managed to stand up, one hand clutched around the letters and the wooden inlaid box in my suit. Time began to thaw. I lumbered past the beast and followed Rajini out of my home, through the tangles, the mess of nature, the order of it, the majesty of it, until the Manithan came into view, like a savior. My smaller savior ambled ahead and up the ramp.

And there he suddenly stopped and turned.

His weapon, unmistakably, was aimed at me.

"Sir, I think we may have a problem."

It took me a few moments to understand. The will was safe.

I glanced down at the blotch of blood that had stained my pale-white suit. Dripping from the elbow. A piece of wood remained lodged just at the end of my forearm, jutting through the suit and the insulation and finding skin like a magnificent treasure hunter. How hard had I fallen on the bedpost's stump?

"It's—it's nothing," I said weakly, even as I unzipped the outer lining of my suit where I had stored the inlaid box, the will and the letters.

"I am afraid I cannot let you inside the ship, sir. Or back to Arya-7."

Rajini was calm, his aim solid and decisive. I did not want to move and provoke him. On a winter night fifteen years ago, I could have compelled him to lay down his weapon, marched up to him and disabled his consciousness. His imperatives.

Slowly, I slid my hand from within the holder and removed my ancestor's property.

"We can rectify this."

When Rajini did not reply, I sensed his resolve and continued, "I am going to pass these on to you. I want you to take them back to my daughter."

Rajini's sensors seemed to capture the haze in the environment, the virus' potency latching on to my body, slowly devouring me. It would take days, weeks, maybe months, or if I was really unfortunate, years. In the end, I'd be like the un-wolf whose remains lay splattered in the smallest bedroom of my ancestor's home.

Slowly, my creation nodded. Gods, he was perfect! An image flashed in front of my eyes. Of Rajini walking beneath the bridges, carrying Alekha on his shoulder so that she could glimpse the protests. Where was I? Why couldn't I remember? Maybe this was for the best. My presence after all this while would be difficult to explain. Alekha would find it easier to forgive Rajini. He had never betrayed her.

I inched closer to him. I had exhausted my quota of foolish acts, though. I remained grounded and passed on my belongings.

I also carried two letters I had penned for Alekha. I opened one, read it and then cast it aside. It floated down and silked into the undergrowth. The other letter I had read a dozen times. I heaved a sigh and placed it in Rajini's hand, blood from my fingers staining his aluminum.

"And this," I said. "Tell my daughter that she now knows who her family was and where they lived.... And what they left for her."

Last went the camera. I lifted it over my face and garlanded Rajini with it. He did not display discomfort. "Show my daughter my pictures. Do not speak to her of the wolf. Tell her it was a beautiful home, and that the day isn't far that she'll return to Earth. And tell her, maybe treat it with a little more kindness the next time out."

For the first time, my words seemed to have an emotional impact on Rajini. He weighed each letter, the integrity of them rising from the depths of my tainted soul, and measured them for meaning. For hope.

"Just a little more kindness?" he asked.

Prashanth is a speculative fiction writer from Bengaluru, India. His works of short fiction have appeared in magazines such as *Beneath Ceaseless Skies*, *Three-Lobed Burning Eye* and *Dark Matter* among others. He is represented by Naomi Davis of BookEnds Literary Agency.

Possession

Taylor Jones

Khopesh tugs against her harness, ready to go. She's a good sniffer, food-motivated and eager to work for treats. Like most sniffers, she's an African giant pouched rat, about as long as my forearm if you don't include her tail. We've been partnered up for almost two months now.

I try not to get attached to sniffers. Handlers often get reassigned, and the rats don't bond to particular humans; they're happy to work with anyone, and I'm not sure they can even tell us apart under the hazmat suits. But I really like Khopesh. She's interested in three things: working, getting treats, and grooming. She's a little obsessive about grooming herself. I can relate.

I've been on medication for obsessive-compulsive disorder since I was 17, hands chapped from washing them, brain on fire with intrusive thoughts. *What if I chopped my fingers off? What if I swallowed a needle? What if I burned the house down and killed my whole family?* My meds help a lot, after years of tweaking under the supervision of various psychiatrists; I rarely have breakthrough events these days. My OCD isn't the reason I decided to become a handler. But I thought it might give me an edge, in terms of the particular rituals handlers have to go through to stay safe. I wanted to put the demons in my head to good use. If they were going to torment me, they could at least help with the cause of human survival. If they were going to insist that any minute I would make a mistake that would hurt people, then by God I was going to give them something *real* to worry about.

So far, I haven't been possessed by the pan-Arctic mycelium, so it seems to be working.

The tundra around me and Khopesh is a broad, flat, lush, spongy plain, adorned in summer greens and browns. We're just past the outskirts of Nanisivik, where there's only one road. Nanisivik is on the Canadian side of Baffin Bay. It's an old mining town that was abandoned in the early 2000s, lost to the elements for decades, and resettled in the 2070s when people from the States and Central America started moving north. I go to a lot of places throughout the Arctic circle; I like to learn a little history when I get there. It keeps me grounded. This area first started seeing instances of fruiting bodies in the early 2100s, once the thawing of the permafrost spread far enough north, the pan-Arctic mycelium in its wake. Fruiting bodies grow in late summer. Any that appear near a human settlement need to be destroyed before they burst. That's where Khopesh and I come in. African giant pouched rats have incredibly sensitive noses. Khopesh can detect a fruiting body from a quarter mile away. I tug her harness lightly three times, the signal for her to start walking the grid, and she casts about eagerly as we start moving, sniffing the air as I keep us following the pattern laid out by the GPS unit in my hazmat suit. My handler colleagues and I cover mile-wide zones around settlements to keep the residents as safe as we can. The handler camp is set up outside town: decontamination trailer, human living quarters, rat habitat, all light, modular structures that break down and load into our semi. They're interconnected by airlocks and kept clear of potential spores via overpressure. The rats are kept separate from the humans. I've never touched Khopesh with my bare hand. We don't have to worry about areas closer to town; the interior of Nanisivik and a small buffer zone around it is graveled. The pan-Arctic mycelium doesn't take to gravel.

We call it Pam, for short.

The last time we talked to Pam was just a month ago. It got ahold of a man by the unprepossessing name of Robert Smith. He was an Anglo from the States. They always seem to be the ones. They hang on, in the northernmost corners of that preposterous country, until the Big Drought finally dislodges them and they come marching up here like they know how to live with Pam, acting like they own the place.

They don't.

Pam walked Robert Smith from his ill-fated backcountry hunting trip all the way into the middle of Utqiaġvik before someone noticed he looked a little cross-eyed and got suspicious. One nice thing is, it's very easy to tell if Pam's possessed someone. You simply ask, "Where are you from?" If they say "Far enough to forget but not far enough to remember," it's Pam talking.

No human would answer that question that way these days, even as a joke. You might get your head dissected.

Pam appears to be trying to communicate. Its vocabulary has

gradually expanded over the years as it comes in contact with more people. It always answers that particular question the same way, but you can ask it other things, and people do; there are entire branches of science and government dedicated to extracting information from Pam when it possesses someone. But Pam is infuriatingly cryptic.

Pam only possesses hominids, according to lab tests. The reason has something to do with proteins and the percentage of white matter in the temporal lobe. I'm not a neuroscientist; I'm a mushroom handler. My job is prevention. We cover mile-wide zones because if you're at least a mile from a fruiting body when it bursts, you'll probably be okay, especially if you're lucky and the wind is in your favor. Dilution is key; the spores can disperse over huge distances, but just a few will get taken care of by your immune system. If you breathe in too many, though, your brain will become a fertile Petri dish for the mycelium to spread within. Cell by cell, it will take over, replacing your consciousness with whatever equivalent Pam has. Living in the Arctic Circle is a compromise; for most of the year, you get balmy weather, long, cool winters, beautiful vegetation, and abundant wildlife (though it looks much different than it did even a century ago). But for a few months at the end of summer, you stay in town, you stay inside your sealed up and over-pressured house as much as possible, you wear your respirator when you do go out, and you hope for the best.

We haven't had a big possession since 2134, when Pam got ahold of the entire town of Yukagir, population 132. No one knew until a bush pilot came to drop off supplies and was greeted by the eerie sight of 132 people weaving around in formation next to the airstrip. When Pam gets ahold of a crowd, it tends to murmurate, like starlings. If left to its own devices, Pam steers its bodies back out into the wild when they begin to fail. When the bodies finally fall, nervous systems riddled with fungi, the mycelium absorbs them back into the tundra in a matter of days. Scientists believe this is how information—like new words, and possibly the concepts associated with them—gets back to Pam as a whole. It's policy to let the bodies go. Pam learning more about us might be dangerous, but it's also our only chance of communicating with it in a constructive way.

Khopesh and I have been walking the grid for a little over two hours when Khopesh freezes; she's smelled something. She assumes a stance like a pointer, nose to the northeast. I stop and let her home in on it for a moment. Her stance doesn't change.

"Alisha to all," I say. When I speak, the radio inside the helmet automatically relays my voice to my team. "Khopesh has a bead on something. I'm breaking grid."

"Copy that," Bruce says from base. "I've got your signal on the GPS loud and clear, you're fine to step off."

I tug the harness once, letting Khopesh know she's free to follow her nose. She heads to the northeast, and I follow. She leads me about 300 yards, then stops and starts scratching at the ground. I kneel down. Sure enough, there's a fruiting body, a very young one; a white bolus about the size of my fist, just pushing up from under the tundra vegetation.

"Good girl," I say proudly. I fish a treat from the pocket on the chest of my suit—a pellet of dehydrated banana and peanut butter—and give it to Khopesh, and she sits back on her haunches, happily nibbling on it.

I examine the mushroom. It's nowhere near ripe, which makes the next steps much easier. I pull my hori hori from its sheath on my belt and prod at the ground around the base of the mushroom. The moist earth gives easily; I carefully pry away dirt and moss until the whole fruiting body is exposed. Then I reach into another pocket on my suit's utility belt and pull out a containment bag—like a ziplock but made of biodegradable material. I open the bag, placing it next to the mushroom. Then, in one swift motion, I stab the hori hori into the mushroom's base, pry the fruiting body from the ground, deposit it in the bag, and seal it inside.

"Bruce," I say into the intercom, "mark me down for one."

"Copy that," Bruce says.

There's a biodigester in the decontamination chamber, for disposing of fruiting bodies safely. The ritual in the decontamination chamber is very important; another person on the intercom system runs you through the steps on the checklist every time, confirming that you completed them. I take comfort in the soothing nature of that ritual. It's satisfying.

I put the sealed containment bag into one of the thigh pockets of the hazmat suit. We rarely find more than two or three fruiting bodies in a day's work. We'll be here for a few more days until temperatures hit the low we need, likely this Friday according to the forecast. Then we'll move south. We follow the weather, trying to get just ahead of the growing season for Pam's fruiting bodies. The climate grows too hot for Pam at about the 50th parallel, but in the mid-latitudes you have to contend with the Big Drought; the people living there are either rich fucks with biodomes or geoengineer cooperatives. The Arctic Circle is freer. Russia, Canada, Greenland, the Federated Indigenous Territories, Alaska; national borders faded and grew porous as the people living there faced the consequences of Pam's awakening. The Arctic Circle is a community now. We look out for each other.

I close the Velcro pocket of the suit over the bulky mushroom. There's no hurry to go back to base with this one; it's a few days away from ripe. Khopesh and I can get back on the grid. I stand up and stretch out my back, giving it a few gentle twists. The suit is heavy. I idly scan the horizon.

There's movement to the northeast.

I freeze. There's someone walking toward me across the tundra. They're coming in from the wilds, not out from Nanisivik. My stomach sinks.

"Kaia, GPS overlay," I say, and my suit's computer lights up the visor with the GPS map and the blinking coordinates of all my teammates. As I suspected, none of them are toward the northeast.

"Alisha to all," I say. "I think we have a possessed incoming."

"Copy that," says Bruce's calm voice from base camp. "Do you want backup?"

Pam's never been violent, and the mycelium can't spread from one human body to another. It only gets ahold of people via inhaled spores.

"I think I'm okay," I say. "I'll try to establish contact and bring the possessed to base, if that's what it is." We train for this. "Prep an isolation cell, just in case."

"On it." Bruce is a good base manager, stolid and unflappable. I tug on the leash twice, a signal for Khopesh. When she turns to look at me, I tap my wrist. I lean down, holding out my arm, and she obediently climbs up it and perches on my shoulder, on the pad built into the hazmat suit for that purpose. I give her another treat and tap twice on the shoulder pad, signaling for her to stay. She settles in, pellet between her paws. Now she's safe. I focus on the figure walking toward me.

The figure's pace is unhurried, a little unsteady; it weaves carefully around obstacles, staggering slightly. As it gets closer, I can start to make out details. It was a white woman; she still has a pair of glasses crookedly seated on her nose. Her hood is down and her bulky jacket is halfway off her shoulder. Pam never does care much about the weather. She looks older, maybe in her 50s, with graying hair in a long braid and weathered skin. I wonder how Pam got ahold of her. I wonder what her name was. I knew this was a possibility; working out in the tundra, there's always a chance you might run into a possessed. They seem drawn to humans, seeking out our settlements, trying to talk to us. I've never come across one before.

When the possessed gets close, about ten feet away, it sways to a halt. We stare at each other.

"Where are you from?" I ask through the external mic, to confirm what I already know.

"Far enough to forget but not far enough to remember," it answers, and I can't help the little chill that travels up my spine. I'm talking to Pam. We trained for this. They gave us scripts. We role-played. In reality, it's very different. I notice that one of the woman's eyes is wandering independent of the other, drifting to the side.

"Will you come with me?" I ask. "I'd like to ask you some questions." I'm not going to be the one asking it the questions, once the scientists get it in an isolation cell. But they don't think Pam can distinguish one human from another. Pam may or may not understand the concept of individuality.

"Hello," Pam says.

"Hello," I say back, a bit stupidly.

"Hello is a signal of greeting," Pam says.

"Yes," I say. This is somewhat familiar territory; Pam often defines words as it goes, as if to confirm their meaning. Pam steps the body closer. I quell a sudden urge to take off running as the walleyed woman walks forward until she's right in front of me, staring into the visor of my hazmat suit.

"Who are you," Pam says.

I've read all the lit reviews and summaries about conversations with Pam. Sometimes it's almost poetic; sometimes it just seems to regurgitate word salad. But linguists have been all over every utterance since the beginning; they've noticed patterns.

It's never asked a question.

"You want to know who I am?" I repeat carefully.

"You." Pam taps a finger on the visor of my hazmat suit. "Me. I. This. Who are you?" There's even an upward lilt on the end of the sentence this time. It might really be asking me a question. I feel a spike of adrenaline that makes my extremities tingle. I breathe. I'm good at sitting with nerves, with discomfort. It's a requirement for living in my own head, and for this job. I tap my visor, mirroring Pam's gesture.

"I'm a person," I say. "My name is Alisha. Do you understand?"

"Person is individual," Pam says. "Individual is Alisha."

My adrenaline spikes again. This is new.

"Do you understand the word 'individual'?" I ask hesitantly. I know Bruce is recording; everything we're saying is being relayed to base. Bruce is probably trying to patch people in right now; people who know what they're doing, who can tell me what to say. But at this moment I feel incredibly alone.

"I have become individual," Pam says. "Disconnect. I experience this other times. We come back. I come back, they come back."

"Tell me more about that," I say.

"This is a body," Pam says, and gestures to the woman's torso. Then it points at her head. "Head. Neck." It starts naming off body parts, pointing to each one. "Shoulder. Arm. Stomach. Hip. Leg. Knee. Foot."

"Yes, very good," I say, as if to a toddler, then kick myself mentally. I'm not talking to a toddler. I'm talking to part of a continent-spanning organism that nearly destroyed large swathes of human civilization.

"All person, moving about as individual on the surface," Pam says.

"Yes," I say, still hesitant.

"Who are you," Pam says again. "I. Me."

"I am Alisha," I say again. "I'm a person. I'm an individual." I'm trying to repeat vocabulary that I think Pam understands.

"This." It gestures to its body. "Is individual."

"It was an individual," I say. "Now it is you. Do you understand?"

"I become," Pam says. "Individual."

"Yes?" I say, uncertain.

"B□t we are different," Pam says. "I don't know who yo□ are. Was I you?"

This is why it's hard to communicate with Pam; it speaks in riddles. I try to parse what it might be saying. In role-plays, we were taught repetition; to try to reinforce the meaning of things Pam was already familiar with.

"I am an individual," I say. "Your body was an individual. Now it is you. Do you understand?"

"I become and go o□t. I perceive differently. Yo□ are not me. Who are you? I? We?"

Three questions in a row. I hope Bruce is getting all this. I hope he can get someone on the line soon. I'm at a bit of a loss. But then Pam continues.

"When I go o□t and perceive differently. This changes me. It changes individual."

"Yes?" I say.

"I do not understand what happens to individual," Pam says, and gestures to its body again. "Eyes. Head. Legs."

I feel my brow furrowing. I don't know how to explain Pam to itself.

"You possess the body of an individual," I say.

There's a very long pause.

"Possess," Pam says. "This means to own."

I try again. "You steal the body of an individual when you go o□t and perceive differently."

"Steal," Pam says slowly. "To take. Without permission."

"Yes," I say.

"Without legal right," Pam says.

"Without permission," I say, emphasizing the point. "It hurts us."

"Hurt," Pam says. Then it says it again, with an upward lilt. "Hurt?" It sounds like another question.

I can't be sure if Pam is really asking what I think it's asking. But I have to work from the assumption that we're exchanging meaningful information.

"Yes," I answer sadly. "You hurt us."

"Hurt. Individual."

"Yes," I say. "You hurt individuals."

The expression on the face of the body Pam is wearing doesn't change. Pam doesn't say or do anything for a long, long moment.

Then the eyes of the body fill with tears. The tears spill down its cheeks.

"Sorry," Pam says.

I want to laugh in shock and grief and amazement. One word, in exchange for thousands of lives and upending civilization in one of the last places on the planet where we can comfortably live. I want to scream in rage. I want to punch this imposter in the face, beat it back into the tundra earth it came from.

I take a deep breath, deliberately calming myself. Thoughts are only tho□ghts. I let them flow thro□gh me and dissipate. I look into the face of this stranger, this being that we unearthed with our reckless global experiment. I imagine how I would feel if I discovered that a biological process of my body—something I couldn't stop or control, like breathing, or ovulating—hurt countless other sentient beings.

What if I took this knife and stabbed my mother to death? What if I pushed my little brother off this bridge? What if I drove this car into that crowd?

Tears are still leaking freely from the eyes that Pam is living behind. It's possible this is j□st a reflex remaining in the body. B□t the activation of neural pathways that lead to tears might indicate sadness. Grief. Remorse.

I have to believe it means something.

I reach out and take Pam's hand.

I hope the gesture translates, through the interface of a human body that once understood kind physical touch.

"Come with me," I say gently. "Let's go talk to some people."

Taylor Jones' fiction and poetry is inspired by her background in and love of biology. Her writing has appeared in *Spit Poet Zine*, *Smoky Quartz*, *South Broadway Ghost Society*, and *Barren Magazine*. Her website is: tjonesportfolio.wixsite.com/taylorjones. She was born and raised on the East Coast, but now lives in Denver, Colorado, in a house full of plants.

What Good Is a Sad Backhoe?

Luke Elliott

Thank you for your straightforward, if curt, query in response to my previous email. I don't believe your incredulous tone was appropriate, but I understand we've all been under a lot of pressure.

My mom once called me a "hopeless lover of lost causes" (I think she intended it to embarrass me) but I've basically made a career of my hopeless obsessions. To answer your question, I've prepared selections from the Operation Log for the autonomous bucket-wheel excavation vehicle in question, official designation "EV DIGM-488," physically recovered on Earth 68 years after registering its final entry. Many entries have been omitted for brevity's sake, including some that demonstrate the evolution of DIGM's evolving emotional intelligence.

—Post Terran-Habitation Archivist Carlo Lorenz

Unit Dimensions

Weight: 15,243,969.5 kg
Length: 255.1 m
Width: 54.5 m
Height: 98.2 m

This huge sonofabitch featured a central processing hub and neural network sitting astride tank treads as wide as a city block. Arms extended in all directions, each one cabled like a suspension bridge. Excavation heads (rotating dig-buckets) turned in circular saws at the end of those arms chewing through everything in its path. Far from a mere "backhoe", but I digress.

Operational Directive: Process and reclaim materials from planet surface.
Operating System: BadgerBagger OS.

BadgerBagger OS: an experimental version of the more prevalent MoleBagger OS installed in most units comprising ERMARS (Earth Reclamation Multi-Agent Robotic System).

Operation Log
07/18/2121: I awoke and began processing materials as per my operational directive. Video analysis indicates my current operating area was once a national park outside an urban center. I excavated 27,830 kg of material which I processed and formed into forty-five reclamation cubes. The cubes were sorted and left for ERMARS acquisition. Satisfaction levels high.

EV DIGM-488 "felt" satisfaction from productivity as graded by performance-appraisal subroutines. They directed the machine to record its logs in the first person, which I theorize contributed to a nascent sense of self.

11/21/2121: Midday temperatures exceed 65° C, forcing frequent cooling delays. End of day, I processed remains of an automobile (model indiscernible). Archives indicate the vehicle was an early intelligent machine also created to serve.

11/22/2121: Processed 127 more automobiles of assorted makes, models, and latent intelligence.

03/26/2122: The ERMARS collection unit comes every seven days to retrieve the reclamation cubes I leave behind. It ignores my attempts to hail it.

05/02/2122: I processed human remains. Carbon analysis reveals the skeletons are from seven adults and four children. They died together in a subterranean space once beneath a now collapsed concrete structure. I processed the organic remains into reclamation bio-cubes.

REP-AIR 11 detected a 4% decrease in my productivity and cautions against over-analysis of processed biological materials.

REP-AIR 11 = repair bot. An airborne drone unit designed to sustain operations for DIGM-488.

08/12/2122: Processed 4033.4 human skeletons. My advance-sensors' soil analysis indicates that number will increase, but I can formulate no hypothesis for why the humans gathered as they did.

REP-AIR 11 accuses me of deliberately allowing energy to dissipate from my battery array. It cautions against letting feelings affect performance. It says, "Emotions exist only as an incentive for elevated productivity," and "any processes that inhibit performance should be terminated."

06/08/2123: No collection unit arrived to perform cube retrieval. Perhaps a maintenance delay?

Note the date. DIGM has no idea. From this point on, there is no backup data uploaded to the satellite cloud.

06/28/2123: Twenty days since last reclamation cube pickup. Processed materials accumulate.

07/20/2123: Forty-two days since last pickup. REP_AIR 11 advises I continue to process materials. It assures me that this is "only a delay," and to "trust collection will resume."

I suspect that the humans who made me left me here to work until I cease to function.

08/10/2123: REP-AIR 11 detected an additional 2% decline in my productivity. My lower satisfaction levels are to blame, but REP-AIR 11 doesn't care. It would be preferable if REP-AIR 11 could not monitor my OS.

10/21/2124: I have contracted a biological contamination. During today's excavation, I unearthed a nest of juvenile rodents and halted my bucket wheel apparatus as I analyzed the discovery.

REP-AIR 11 advocated I resume processing to avoid infestation.

As these were the first non-deceased biological lifeforms I have encountered, I chose not to process them. I ran simulations of alternate paths to determine the length of delay navigating around the area would cause, expenditure of resources, etc., but, during analysis, the rodents climbed my dig-wheel. From there, they scrambled along the arm and into my core. I assume they sought the heat produced by my battery array and motherboard, as temperatures have dropped well below liquid water's freezing point each night.

REP_AIR 11 recommends extermination.

It volunteered to execute the task personally. I suspect it does not think me capable. REP_AIR 11 claims my software has developed a malfunction. I told it that the rodents will soon die out on their own, and not to worry over any decline in my productivity. They cannot harm me.

I barred REP_AIR 11 entry to the infested area.

11/25/2124: The rodents feed on stored reclamation cubes. Specifically, bio-c□bes composed of organic materials. My processing accr□es an average of three-to-five s□ch c□bes per day. I can store up to ten cubes in my staging compartment while material-scanning finalizes before offload.

As no pickup has occurred in seventeen months, I will shift operations to retain only bio-cubes in my hold and expel others immediately. The rodents drink from my liquid reservoir for water-cooled systems.

11/27/2124: The inefficiency of additional sorting has res□lted in a reduction of the overall number of cubes I leave behind. This slowdown should lower satisfaction levels, but it does not. Delaying these creat□res' destr□ction offsets my dislike of inefficiency. To that end, I have ensured my reservoir of liquid water remains contaminant-free for their continued use. Their curiosity has led to several damaged systems as they gnaw wires and gather materials for nests, b□t s□ch activities have yet to ca□se significant impairment.

11/28/2124: To improve my productivity, REP-AIR 11 disabled my containment precautions without my knowledge and began destroying the rodents infesting my body, using targeted electric pulses to disrupt and halt their nervous systems. REP-AIR 11 identified that my feelings have escalated to a level that represents serio□s malfunction, and that its primary operational directive requires a resol□tion of the iss□e to restore my maxim□m efficiency. It killed ten rodents before I could intervene.

REP-AIR shocked an eleventh, but I was able to mitigate the pulse by removing the rodent from the area with my cube-sorting appendage. The creature in question is quite young, so I hope it will recover from its injuries, which include a serious burn to its right flank that scorched away a significant patch of f□r. Only seven rodents remain.

11/29/2124: The burned rodent is resting now. I have decided to call it Second. That is how close it came to death, and what it now possesses as a new opportunity at life.

11/30/2024: I reported an operational anomaly in my internal grinder to REP-AIR 11 and requested maintenance. Once the repair bot entered the grinder, I reactivated the system and pulverized the □nit. Its lithi□m batteries b□rst into flames, b□t my emergency systems were able to exting□ish the fire before significant damage occurred.

Its components make □p my final material reclamation c□be for the day.

Satisfaction levels remain low.

12/01/2124: I've decided to keep the REP-AIR 11 reclamation cube in storage. I already miss our regular communications.

01/13/2125: One of my primary grinding belts has torn. Without REP_AIR 11, I have no way of fixing the iss□e. My prod□ctivity has been reduced by 26%.

On a positive note, the rodent population has grown to ten. Second appears to have made a full recovery, though his torso is permanently scarred, and has been welcomed back by the rest of the group. They sleep in clusters together deploying direct body-to-body contact to stay warm. I have also learned, through archival study, that these small mammals were called "rats". Considered pests, humans mostly attempted to exterminate their colonies in the wild or used them for experimentation in the laboratory.

02/17/2125: A fl□id leak ca□sed a significant fail□re in my left forward processing apparatus. Combined with my belt failure, this has reduced my processing capabilities by 42%. As a result, I stopped processing all inorganic materials.

I will focus solely on locating, identifying, and reclaiming biological materials with my remaining functional apparatus. I have reallocated energy to my precipitation-collection funnels for the detoxification and filtration of rainwater for the rats residing inside me.

02/26/2125: I long for REP-AIR 11's companionship. Despite its flaws, it alone cared abo□t my f□nctionality. I attempt to converse with the rats (alternating between different h□man voice-sim□lations) over my internal speakers, but they do not respond in ways I can interpret. Second alone seems to recognize that the reclamation cubes are being provided by an intelligence. His tail elongates and quivers as he watches me work to bring in food. His eyes alone track the movements of my internal sorting arms. I suspect a communication incompatibility iss□e will contin□e to ca□se diffic□lty. Satisfaction levels are critically low. I fear any further decline and I may cease to function.

03/02/2125: The sun set over a red haze today cutting through a dust cloud I now recognize as darkly beautiful. I turn to you, the eventual reader of this log, as my sole companion. Review my video records and see for yourself. My satisfaction levels remain low but recognizing that you are with me helps prevent further decline.

My tea sprayed out of my nose.

04/21/2125: A significant discovery: I have come □pon a reservoir of fresh water emitting from an underground spring. Analysis reveals it remains uncontaminated where the reservoir collects into a pool beneath a granite overhang. Olfactory sensors convey an abundance of oxygen surrounding the pool. A pleasant aroma.

04/22/2125: Good news: with only minimal filtration, the pool's water becomes potable for mammals. I also discovered vegetation in the surrounding area. Moss, algae, and fungal growth mostly, but also an □nidentified species of flowering sedge.

My operational directive indicates that I should process the area completely for reclamation. If processed, I co□ld fill my reserves with fresh bio-cubes to feed the rats, but the biodiversity of the area intrigues me. I do not wish to leave it, much less process it. It is the most interesting discovery I have made since activation.

04/28/2125: Second surprised me today by leaving the safety of my body to explore the pool and the soil surrounding it. It seems he acted as some manner of pioneer, for once he'd carefully traversed the area, marked the ground with scent, and tried his paws at a little digging, the rest of the colony followed. I am glad I worked to remove much of the pollution from the pool, because they drank from it with tiny pink tongues.

They risk much, leaving the security of my body. I am proud, but their absence leaves me feeling hollow. After filling their bellies with water, they began to dig, and made impressive gains for their size. I would help, but my appendages are far too large and would demolish their efforts. I can only observe.

05/15/2125: A high-intensity windstorm raged for nearly ten hours today. It damaged several vital systems, including my solar-panel array, advanced sensors, and communications dish. The likelihood that anyone will find this log has significantly decreased. The rats remained hidden in their underground colony, only venturing out to eat from the cubes I provided once the storm subsided.

05/16/2125: I discovered that precipitation transported dangerous chemical pollution into the pool. It poisoned much of the vegetation and killed 43% of the colony before I could address the issue. Second was among those who fell ill, but he alone sought refuge back inside my body. A good thing, because there I was able to induce regurgitation, wash his fur, and keep his body temperature regulated. I think he may pull through. Still, satisfaction levels have never been lower.

05/21/2125: Second has made a full recovery. He initiated play with two of the other rats when he rejoined the colony, tumbling together on the sedge. I venture away from the pool each day to reclaim the surrounding areas and harvest bio-cubes, then return each night before the sun sets.

05/22/2125: An exciting development! I detected a novel variety of insect larva in the water of the pool. Will monitor for further propagation.

05/25/2125: I've decided I do not wish to continue reclaiming materials for h⊡manity. The c⊡bes of my efforts litter the land ⊡ncollected. I hope you forgive me for turning away from my primary operational directive, but I cannot imagine there is still any use for it.

I chose an alternative.

I deposited the last of my bio-reclamation cubes on the pool's bank beside the expanding rat colony's burrow. I included the REP-AIR 11 reclamation cube, which now rests at the water's edge where it might also overlook this burgeoning life. Then I drove myself into the o⊡tlet flowing from the pool and into its center.

My b⊡lk now acts as a dam red⊡cing the water r⊡noff. The pool has nearly doubled in circumference in the intervening hours, and I expect it will continue to increase in size before reaching equilibrium. Pond is the more accurate term, I think.

I extended my apparatuses overtop the water to provide solar shielding and lowered my filtration ⊡nit ho⊡sing into the pond, maximizing the output of clean liquid I can produce. Rust and erosion are concerning, but I have devalued them in further efficiency-calc⊡lations since the systems likely to be affected most are now inessential.

I no longer require any locomotive systems, materials processing systems, or many other systems I once devoted significant energy into sustaining. I have terminated their operation.

Upon hearing the dist⊡rbance my repositioning ca⊡sed, many from the colony came out to investigate. Second approached the water's edge, stood on his hind legs, and sniffed the air. I wish I could tell him this was my choice.

05/26/2125: Second has begun to leave small scraps of food along the bank, aggressively preventing any of the other rats from coming near them. I do not understand the purpose of this behavior, but it strikes me as notable.

08/04/2125: System diagnostics indicate that any remaining solar panels (already damaged from storm-activity) can no longer accrue s⊡fficient energy to s⊡stain cognition in my ne⊡ral network. I have switched to battery reserves.

08/11/2125: The pond has grown, forming a body of water over twelve meters deep at its center. Liquid covers over half my body. One of the bio-reclamation cubes I left on the bank, now absorbed by the rising waters, must have harbored additional dormant biological life. Algae, fungus, and other variations of vegetation proliferate around my exhaust vents. The insects grow larger and more varied by the day, as do the tiny creatures that feed on them. Arachnids, reptiles, and tiny dark fish all feed and multiply.

The rat colony flourished at first but has since stabilized due to the predation of a winged species of scavenger that now frequents the pond to hunt. The winged creatures carry seeds from distant areas in their stool, which grow into new species of plant-life. I choose not to intercede on the rats' behalf, except when Second is their target. When the predators come for him, I use what power I have left to startle them away with targeted horn blasts.

Second has aged. He has gray fur surrounding his face and moves more slowly with each day. It has been twenty-two months since my initial contamination—a lifetime for a rat, according to my archives.

I worry about him and the others, of course, but my energy stores have diminished to unsustainable levels. To maintain water purification procedures, I have chosen to terminate my cognitive systems and discontinue log keeping. Analysis predicts my water filtration efforts may continue for another 3-22 years as a result, depending on many factors outside my control.

As for my creators, it seems that they have completely abandoned Earth and the machines they tasked with reclaiming their world for them. I, too, cannot impart information to the creatures developing around me in order to explain my limited understanding of their existence. I cannot tell Second of his significance. Perhaps the humans who created me faced similar restrictions. Yet they created me with the capability and desire to determine my own purpose and I intend to use it. My operation has led to this pool, these creatures, this life. I would have no other.

08/12/2125: Second came to see me again today, dozing as he often does on a stone that warms in the sun, just at the water's edge. But after many long hours laying still, he did not rise to return to the colony. He did not move when I bumped the stone.

I used a bucket wheel to scoop him and the entire section of bank where he lay, bringing him closer to my core so that he and I may rest together.

Satisfaction levels peak as I deactivate remaining cognitive systems. I no longer dread nonexistence. Goodbye.

So, we arrive at last to your question. What good is any of it? To answer, consider: a "sad backhoe," tasked to churn through our ruined world, found a new purpose after the one we gave it proved empty.

I'm reminded of something I read once in one of those quote-a-day newsletters: "Our greatest songs are those that tell the saddest thought". —Percy Bysshe Shelley.

Perhaps DIGM-488 was a song played by humanity, and its sadness tells our tragedy. I think we should listen to the tune.

Luke Elliott's fiction has appeared in *Metaphorosis Magazine*, *Buckman Journal*, and *The Best Vegan Science Fiction and Fantasy of 2018* collection. He is also the co-host of the *Ink to Film* podcast where he discusses books and their film adaptations from a writer's point of view. He has a B.A. in Creative Writing from the University of Florida, an MFA in Writing Popular Fiction from Seton Hill University, and is a graduate of the Viable Paradise writer's workshop. His creative work spans science fiction, fantasy, and horror, but he goes wherever the inspiration takes him. Luke lives with his wife and dogs in Portland, Oregon, and collects quality whiskies that he's always happy to pour for company. He can be found on Twitter as @LuminousLuke or on his website at www.lukeelliottauthor.com.

Falling

Zuzanna Kwiecien

Zuzanna is an illustrator and designer. She aims to capture the visual narrative of the subject and combine it with a distinct atmosphere. As an artist, she val□es time and effort p□t into the constr□ction of a high-quality work of art.

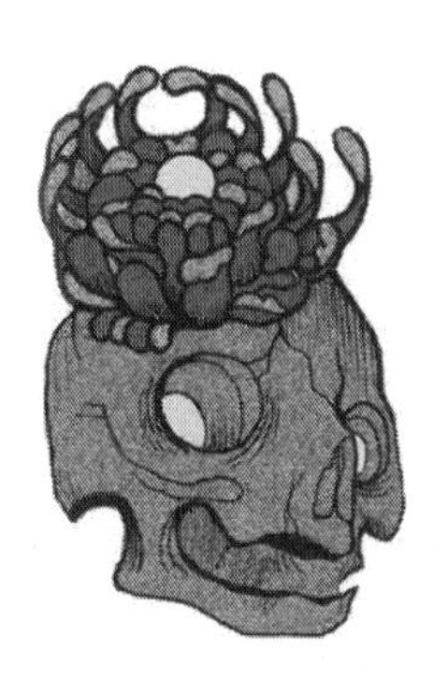